WHISKEY DISTILLER'S TRAINING MANUAL

Christopher G. Yorke, M. Ed

Mason Creek Publishing

Whiskey Distiller's Training Manual

By Christopher G. Yorke, M. Ed

Published by:
Mason Creek Publishing
35111 NE 94th Ave.
La Center, WA 98629
(360)263-5780
cyorke57@gmail.com

Copyright 2017 by Mason Creek Publishing

ISBN: 978-0-9986005-0-5
Printed in the United States of America
Library of Congress CIP Data Pending

Cover art by Sandra Yorke
blueowlstudio.biz

Money Back Guarantee
If the Whiskey Distiller's Training Manual does not meet your expectations for any reason, return it to Mason Creek Publishing for a 100% refund. Book must be returned in good condition within 30 days of purchase date. Be sure to include your return address.

TESTIMONIALS

Comments made by people who have consumed spirits made using the procedures in the Whiskey Distiller's Training Manual.

"This stuff is as good as you said it was."
  - Dave Carlile, Yacolt, WA

"We love it."
  - Alex Collins, Portland, OR

"A very unique flavor with exceptional quality."
  - Tod Garred, Battle Ground, WA

"It's an olfactory sensation."
  - Tim Hicks, Brush Prairie, WA

"The single malt whiskey is like drinking silk."
  - Kevin Kernen, Vancouver, WA

"The smokey bourbon has an especially good smooth taste."
  - Steve McNeal, Battle Ground, WA

"It's amazing."
  - Josh Simpson, Vancouver, WA

"The single malt was surprisingly smooth."
  - Jason Susee, Vancouver, WA

"The chocolate malt whiskey was amazing."
  - Jason Susee, Vancouver, WA

Whiskey Distiller's Training Manual Contents

The items in this chapter are grouped in order to provide a more consistent flow of information. The same items are listed alphabetically in the glossary for quick reference.

Chapter 2 - Equipment and Supplies, Setup and Use - Page 11

Chapter 3 - Whiskey Grain Bills and Recipes - Page 52

INTRODUCTION

The purpose of the Whiskey Distiller's Training Manual is to get you up and running now. Everything you need to know is in this manual. You won't need to read four different books or spend countless hours searching the internet for the information you need - it is ALL here. There are many different approaches to distilling alcohol and making whiskey. This manual contains the basic concepts and the proven procedures you need in order to successfully make your own spirits, including clear pictures of every step. After you master the basic processes outlined in the manual you can begin to venture out and try new methods and create your own unique whiskey. I recommend that you read through chapters 1 and 2 first in order to get a good general overview of the whiskey making process and all of the supplies and equipment you will be using. Then, in the remaining chapters we will get into the detailed steps and procedures of cooking mash, fermentation, distilling, aging, and bottling. The first 2 chapters may seem a little overwhelming at first. Just push through them and when you get into the later chapters things will start to gel and you will be prepared to make top shelf spirits. Although the concepts covered in the book can be applied to the use of any kind of still, we will be illustrating the use of a copper alembic pot still. It is the oldest type of still, but still considered by many to produce the best, most flavorful whiskey. It is also a good type of still to use when learning the whiskey making process.

Please remember that in order to distill spirits legally you need a license. For a small distiller you can apply for a craft distiller's license. You will need to apply for a Federal license and check with the requirements of your particular State.

Chapter 1

Whiskey and Distillation Basics

Whiskey

The word whiskey comes from the Latin word "aqua vitae," meaning the water of life. Whiskey is a distilled spirit made from fermented grain or any other organic matter containing carbohydrates. The distillate is aged in charred white oak barrels to produce whiskey. Remember that whiskey is a general term for various types of distilled spirits including bourbon, scotch, Tennessee whiskey, Canadian whiskey and Irish whiskey. They are all whiskey, but involve some different production and aging processes. We will cover each kind in more depth later in the book.

Distillation

Distillation is the process of separating substances from a liquid mixture by heating, evaporating (forming a vapor), cooling and condensing vapor back into a liquid. Once the vapor is condensed back into a liquid it is referred to as the distillate. In the case of making whiskey the distillate is alcohol, primarily ethanol. The distillate produced during the whiskey making process starts off clear as water; this is true for any kind of spirit. This would be called moonshine if it were distilled at night in the "shine of the moon."

The Process of Making Whiskey

This is a very short description of the whiskey-making process to get us started. First, a mixture of grains, or other organic biomass, is mixed with water and cooked to form a mash. The mash is cooled and yeast is added so that sugars in the mash can be converted into alcohol (fermentation). The resulting fermented liquid (wash), which now contains alcohol, is heated in order to separate the various kinds of alcohol out of the wash (distillation). The distillate is aged with charred or toasted oak to produce whiskey. Again, this is a very short description. We will get deeper into the process as we proceed. Also note that this process is basically the same, with some variations, for whiskey, bourbon, rum, vodka and single malt whiskey (Scotch).

Moonshine

Moonshine is illegal whiskey made at home. It can be made of any kind of organic matter, however, moonshine is typically made from corn mash and is not aged. Back during the days of prohibition, between 1920 and 1933, the production and sale of liquor (spirits) was illegal in the United States. People would illegally distill spirits at night, in the "shine of the moon," to avoid being caught by the law. The term is thought to have originated in England. Early English whiskey smugglers were called "Moonrakers" because they worked by the light of the moon. You can find whiskey called Moonshine in liquor stores, but it is not actually moonshine. It is simply white dog (white whiskey) that has not been aged in an oak barrel.

All distilled spirits start off as plain old ethanol, including moonshine. Ethanol is the good part of the distillate that can be made into whiskey and consumed. The various kinds of alcohol, including ethanol, come out of the still as clear as water. It's the different grains, the aging process, and filtration techniques that turn the ethanol into whiskey.

Grain

Grain refers to the seed produced by plants in the grass family (gramineae). Most distilled spirits are made from grains including corn, barley, rye, wheat, oats and triticale. Although spirits can be made from pretty much any kind of organic matter containing carbohydrates, the grains are the most popular.

Grain Anatomy

It is important to have a basic knowledge of grain anatomy in order to understand how alcohol is produced from fermented grains. Refer to the picture below as we discuss grain anatomy. This diagram shows a generic example of a grain (seed). It could be barley, rye, oats, or wheat. Although corn is also in the gramineae family, its structure is a little different that the other grains. The endosperm contains starch (carbohydrates). When water enters the seed, enzymes are activated that convert the starch to glucose (simple sugar). The embryo (germ), which is an immature plant, feeds on the glucose and water and begins to grow (germination).

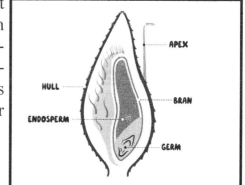

When we cook our mash we are allowing the natural enzymes in the grain, plus additional enzymes we add, to convert the starch into glucose. This is the process of saccharification. After the mash cools we add yeast which consumes the glucose (fermentation). As the yeast ferments the glucose it produces alcohol and carbon dioxide.

Glucose, Maltose, Maltotriose

Glucose, maltose and maltotriose are the components of the starches found in the endosperm of cereal grains. Glucose ($C_6H_{12}O_6$) is the simplest sugar and is known as a monosaccharide meaning one glucose molecule. Maltose ($C_{12}H_{22}O_{11}$) is a disaccharide with two glucose molecules. Maltotriose ($C_{18}H_{32}O_{16}$) is a trisaccharide consisting of three glucose molecules. These sugars are present in the wort and are used by the yeasts during the process of fermentation.

Corn

The scientific name for corn is Zea mays. There are 6 different types of corn in the Zea mays genus that are produced and used by humans, dent corn, flint corn, pod corn, popcorn, flour corn and sweet corn. Yellow dent corn (Zea mays var. indentata) is the primary corn used for ethanol and therefore whiskey production. Yellow dent corn has a high starch content compared to other varieties and that characteristic makes it good for making spirits.

Barley

The scientific name for barley is Hordeum vulgare. There are two main varieties, 2 row and 6 row. Two row barley has 2 rows of grain kernels on each head. It has a lower protein content, but higher carbohydrate (sugar) content. This is the primary kind used to make barley malt. Six row barley has 6 rows of grain kernels per head. It has more protein and a lower sugar content. It is primarily used as livestock feed.

Malted Barley

Malted barley, or barley malt, is made by soaking barley in water and initiating the germination (sprouting) process. The grain is then heated with hot air in order to stop germination. During this partial germination beta-amylase enzyme is produced inside the grain that helps convert starches in the grain into simple sugars like maltose and glucose. When malted barley is mixed with other grains in the mash the beta-amylase enzyme, plus alpha-amylase enzyme added by the distiller, converts all of the starches from all of the different grains in the mash into glucose. Malted grains, like malted barley, are often referred to as malt, referring to the maltose in the grain.

3

Rye

Rye is another cereal grain in the gramineae family. It's scientific name is Secale cereale. Rye is used to make flour, rye bread, rye beer, whiskey, vodka and is also used as livestock feed. Rye can be used to make rye whiskey, is part of the grain bill in bourbon, and is often used in making Canadian whiskey. It provides a spicy flavor to the whiskey. Early whiskey's in the United States were primarily made of rye since it was grown extensively at the time and was cheap. As the production of other grains like corn increased, other types of whiskey became more popular.

Wheat

Wheat, Triticum aestivum, is the second most produced grain in the world, topped only by corn. There are only a few straight wheat whiskeys produced in the world. However, there are many whiskeys which are "wheated," meaning that a small percentage of the grain bill includes wheat. Wheat tends to make whiskey smoother and sweeter tasting. The flavor profile of wheat whiskey is much milder than whiskey without wheat.

Oats

Oats, Avena sativa, are used to make bread, oatmeal, other baked goods and as livestock feed. There are a few distillers who make oat whiskey. The grain bill is usually 85% oats and 15% barley malt. Oats create a very smooth whiskey with a mellow, sweet, toasted grain flavor.

Grain Bill

In the distilling industry the grain bill is simply a list of which grains are used to make the mash and the percentage of each. For example, the grain bill for Jack Daniels Tennessee Whiskey is 80% corn, 12% rye and 8% malted barley. Of course, trying to make Jack Daniels whiskey isn't just a matter of using their grain bill. They use various techniques in their production process that produces the unique flavors of Jack Daniels, techniques that are closely guarded secrets.

Mash

The mash consists of water, grains and enzymes added to help in the saccharification process. The mash is heated to specific temperatures and is rested for a certain length of time before adding yeast. The mashing process will be explained in greater detail later in the book.

Wort

The wort is the liquid produced from the mashing process. It contains glucose which will be fermented by yeast. By using a sugar hydrometer we can measure the specific gravity of the wort and determine what is known as the potential alcohol level.

Potential Alcohol

This is the amount of alcohol we would expect to be produced from the fermentation of the wort. Most batches of wort will have between 8 and 10% potential alcohol. Again, this process will be explained in complete detail later.

Wash

The wash is the liquid produced after fermentation is completed. The wash will normally contain 8 to 10% alcohol. The wash goes into the still for distillation.

Alcohol By Volume

Alcohol By Volume is usually abbreviate as ABV. It is the concentration of total alcohol, as a percentage, in the distillate or in a bottle of whiskey. For example, 40% ABV.

Proof

Alcohol proof is twice the percentage of alcohol by volume. So, if you have a whiskey that is 40% abv it would be 80 proof.

Alcohols in the Distillate

There are a number of different types of alcohol produced by the yeast during fermentation. When we distill the wash the different kinds of alcohol will vaporize at different temperatures. The list below shows the different alcohols that are distilled out of a typical wash and the temperature at which each is vaporized.

Acetone 56.5°C (134°F)

Methanol 64°C (147°F) - ***Poison***

Ethyl acetate 77.1°C (171°F)

Ethanol 78°C (172°F)

2-Propanol (rubbing alcohol) 82°C (180°F)

1-Propanol 97°C (207°F)

Water 100°C (212°F)

Butanol 116°C (241°F)

Amyl alcohol 137.8°C (280°F)

Furfural 161°C (322°F)

Yeast

Yeasts are the microorganisms that ferment the wort and create alcohol. Yeasts are single-celled microorganisms classified as members of the fungus kingdom. Saccharomyces cerevisiae is the primary species of yeast used in the distillation of spirits. However, there are many strains of yeast used within that species by the different distilleries. I recommend Distiller's Active Dry Yeast (DADY). This is a good all purpose yeast for distilling that works very well. Once you become an experienced distiller you can branch out and try different strains. Adding yeast to the mash is called "pitching" the yeast. Keep your yeast in an airtight container in the refrigerator.

Yeast Nutrients

The source of energy consumed by yeast is glucose, but yeasts also require other nutrients in order to reproduce and grow. Yeast nutrient blends contain a mix of trace elements, inorganic nitrogen, organic nitrogen, zinc and phosphates that helps yeast grow and complete fermentation. Yeast nutrients are added to the mash at the same time as the yeast is pitched.

Yeast Energizer

Yeast energizers contain components such as diammonium phosphate, yeast hulls, magnesium sulfate, vitamin B complexes and tricalcium phosphate. Energizers are used to give a boost to a fermentation that is sluggish or stuck during the fermentation process.

Gelatinization

When using corn meal or polenta as your source of corn in a batch, the corn must first be gelatinized. This involves heating the corn in water which breaks the bonds between the starch molecules. This basically dissolves the starch and allows the corn to absorb more water. Once the corn is gelatinized you can add the remaining grains (e.g., barley malt, rye), and proceed to cook the batch.

Saccharification

The breaking apart of polysaccharides (complex sugars and starches), to soluble sugars like glucose is called saccharification. Malted barley containing beta-amylase enzyme and the addition of alpha-amylase enzyme to the mash, break the starch molecules apart to produce single molecules of glucose (simple sugar). The glucose can then be consumed by the yeast during fermentation.

Fermentation

Fermentation is the process of converting sugars, like glucose and maltose, into acids, carbon dioxide (CO_2) and various alcohols by yeasts. The alcohol we are primarily interested in is ethanol ($2 C_2 H_5 OH$). During both respiration and fermentation yeast cells break down glucose molecules to release energy. This is called glycolysis. The breakdown of glucose also releases carbon atoms which can be used by the yeast to grow and reproduce (budding). It is important to make sure the yeasts have an ample supply of oxygen and other nutrients for efficient fermentation. We will explain this in detail later.

Bacteria

Bacteria are microscopic single-celled organisms. There are many kinds of bacteria, some are harmful, but many are beneficial. There are several species of Lactobacillus bacteria that can enter your mash naturally or can be added intentionally. Lactobacillus will produce various acids that are used in the creation of esters in the wort. The esters will have a flavorful effect on your whiskey. You can purchase Lactobacillus bacteria to incorporate into your mash if desired. You add the bacteria prior to fermentation. For our examples in this book, we will not be adding any bacteria to our mash.

Bourbon

The grain bill for bourbon is corn, barley and rye. It must be at least 51% corn. Most commercial bourbons are made from 70-80% corn, 15-20% barley malt and 5-10% rye. Bourbon must be aged a minimum of 2 years in new charred American White Oak barrels.

Scotch

To be called Scotch, whiskey needs to be made in Scotland. Scotch is made from 100% malted barley. Some Scotches also have some peated barley in the mash. This gives the whiskey the smoky or peaty flavor. Scotch is aged a minimum of three years in charred white oak barrels. The best Scotch is made from a single batch of malted barley and not blended with any other batch. This is called single malt whiskey. In America whiskey made from 100% malted barley is called Single Malt Whiskey since it can't be called Scotch.

Irish Whiskey

Irish whiskey is obviously made in Ireland. The grain bill is 50% barley and 50% barley malt. The big difference is that Irish whiskey is triple distilled. Three distillations give the final product a very clean taste. It is aged in charred white oak barrels.

Rum

Rum is made from sugar and/or molasses. There are three main types of rum: white, gold and dark. White rum is not aged and it is filtered which removes much of the color and flavor. Gold rum is also known as amber rum. It is aged in charred white oak barrels. Dark rum is aged in charred white oak barrels for a longer period of time. Caramelized sugar is often added to add color and flavor.

Vodka

The name vodka comes from the Russian word "voda" which means water. Vodka is usually distilled several times. It is considered to be a neutral spirit, meaning it has very little flavor. Vodka can be made from anything that can be fermented as opposed to whiskey which must be made from grain. Most vodkas are made from grains or potatoes. Most commercial vodka distilleries make their finest vodkas from winter wheat. Vodka is not aged in barrels like whiskey.

Corn Whiskey

The grain bill for corn whiskey must contain at least 80% corn. The remaining 20% is usually malted barley. Corn whiskey must be aged for a minimum of two years in new or used white oak barrels. The barrels don't have to be charred. Corn whiskey is often marketed as "White Lightening."

Single Barrel

Single barrel whiskey, or single cask whiskey, is whiskey that comes from an individual aging barrel, instead of being created by blending together the contents of different barrels.

Small Batch Whiskey

Small batch whiskey is whiskey that is produced by mixing the contents of a small number of selected barrels. So it is blended whiskey.

White Dog

The alcohol that comes out of the still and is placed into aging barrels is called white dog. It has no color and little whiskey flavor at this point. It is the raw distillate.

Sour Mash

Sour mash is mash from a previous batch that is added to a new batch of mash. This adds to the flavor of the whiskey and also helps to control bacteria like Clostridium butyricum which can ruin the batch.

Back Set

The watery part of a previously distilled batch of wash that can be added into the next batch.

Peat and Peated Barley

Peat consists of dead plant material including moss, grasses and tree roots that have been compacted under a layer of soil and decomposed slowly over many years, sometimes thousands of years. The peat is dug up, dried and can be burned for fuel or other uses.

In whiskey making peat is burned underneath a layer of malted barley. The heat from the burning peat stops the germination of the malted barley and dries it out. The peat smoke produces chemicals called phenols that are absorbed by the malted barley and give it a smoky flavor. Peated barley is often used in making Scotch or other malt whiskeys. Regular malted barley is dried without using peat and does not have the smoky smell or flavor.

Foreshots

The first few ounces of distillate produced during a distillation. They contain methanol and other volatile alcohols. They should be discarded. There is a lot of conflicting information about the quantity of foreshots to discard. Some distillers believe foreshots should be removed from both the striping run and the spirit run. Others believe they should be removed from one or the other. I recommend discarding one ounce per gallon of wash from the spirit run. You might be discarding a little more than you really need to, but you're just removing some early heads so it doesn't really matter. You probably don't want to keep them anyway. Better to be on the safe side. So, if we had 7 gallons of wash after fermentation, we would discard the first 7 ounces of foreshots from the spirit run.

Heads

The first major part of the distillate is called the heads. The heads contain compounds like acetone, acetaldehyde, acetate and some ethanol. They have a strong, almost fruity smell and taste harsh. Heads can be discarded or collected and added to the next spirit run. Approximately 20-30% of the liquid collected during a distillation run will be heads.

Hearts

The hearts contain mainly ethanol and are the part of the spirit run we want to collect and make into whiskey. Hearts will have a light sweet smell and a light sweet, smooth taste. Be warned though, hearts still do not taste like whiskey, they are still raw distillate. The skill of the distiller is in developing the ability to smell and taste the different fractions of distillate in order to separate the heads, hearts and tails effectively. Approximately 30-40% of the run will be hearts.

Tails

The tails occur at the end of the run. Tails do contain some ethanol as well as fusel oils like propanol, butanol and amyl alcohol. Tails also contain water, carbohydrates and proteins. You will know when the tails start because they smell like a wet dog and taste muddy. You will also see an oily sheen on top of the distillate as the tails continue to distill and the distillate will start to look cloudy. Tails can be discarded or collected and added to the next spirit run. Tails will make up approximately 20-30% of a spirit run.

Chapter 2

Equipment and Supplies
Setup
Use
Where to Purchase
Cost

ALEMBIC POT STILL AND PARTS

The copper alembic pot still is the oldest type of still used. Many people, including some commercial distilleries, believe the Alembic Copper Still produces the best tasting whiskey. It consists of the still, still head, vapor thermometer, condenser, coiled condenser tubing, (goes down into the condenser) and vapor thermometer. The wash is placed into the still and heated by the burner for distillation. Alcohol vapors accumulate in the still head, travel past the vapor thermometer and into the condenser tubing. As the vapor travels down the condenser tubing into the condenser, the cool water in the condenser converts the vapor back into liquid. The liquefied alcohol exits the condenser through the food-grade condenser discharge tube and goes into a distillate collection jar. I recommend buying a 35 liter (9 Gal.) still. All of my examples in this book will relate to using a 35 liter still. You can purchase one from Iberian Copper's (copper-alembic.com) for $250.00, plus about $65.00 for shipping.

A - 35 liter still   E - Condenser

B - Still head   F - Food grade condenser discharge tube

C - Vapor thermometer   G - Burner

D - Condenser tubing   H - Alcohol Parrot   I - Distillate collection jar

CONDENSER PARTS AND SETUP

The condenser consists of a copper bucket with a coiled copper tube that brings the vaporized distillate from the still down through a supply of cool water. As the vapor enters the coiled copper tubing, which is in the cool water, the vapor returns to a liquid and drains out through the food grade tubing into your distillate collection jar.

A - Water line in, 1/2" black irrigation tubing, with 1/2" hose clamp.
   Brings water into condenser bucket.
B - Water line out, 1/2" black irrigation tubing, with 1/2" hose clamp.
   A long enough pipe to go outside to drain.
C - 1/2" food grade tubing connected with 1/2" hose clamp.
   For distillate outflow to collection jar.

CONDENSER COILED COPPER TUBING

Inside the condenser you find the coiled condenser tubing. During distillation the condenser is full of cool water that continuously flows into the condenser from an inflow line and leaves the condenser through an outflow line. This provides the cool water required to convert the alcohol vapors back into liquid form.

Inside of the condenser showing the coiled tubing.

ALCOHOL PARROT

The alcohol parrot is used to monitor the alcohol by volume (ABV) coming out of the still during distillation. This is very useful because you can watch the ABV continuously as you distill. The setup for the parrot is shown on the next page. You can purchase a parrot for about $35.00 from ebay.

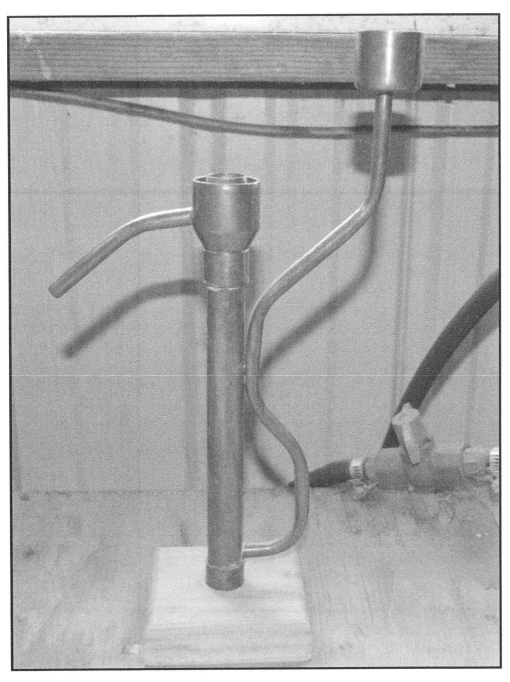

Alcohol Parrot

ALCOHOL PARROT AND DISTILLATE COLLECTION JAR SETUP

The alcohol parrot collects distillate from the food grade distillate tube (A) The alcohol hydrometer is placed into the parrot tube (B). Once the distillate has filled the parrot tube, ABV can be read off of the hydrometer. See "how to use an alcohol hydrometer" on page 18. Distillate flows out of the parrot and into the collection jar.

Alcohol Parrot Setup with distillate collection jar

ALCOHOL HYDROMETER

The alcohol hydrometer or alcoholmeter, measures the specific gravity of the distillate. Once you know the specific gravity you can determine the ABV. Specific gravity indicates how dense a liquid is. Alcohol is less dense than water so the hydrometer will float higher in it compared to water. The picture below shows you how the hydrometer is placed into the alcohol parrot. See page 18 for a complete explanation of how the hydrometer works and how to use it. You can purchase an alcohol hydrometer form brew stores or from Amazon.com for about $12.00.

Alcohol Hydrometer

HOW TO USE AN ALCOHOL HYDROMETER (ALCOHOLOMETER)

The alcohol hydrometer has two scales, one on each side. One side shows the abv percentage and the other shows the proof. Proof is simply twice the abv. For example, 40% abv is 80 proof.

When you place the hydrometer into a parrot, graduated cylinder, or any other receptacle it will float and you can read the abv or proof. If your reading was as shown with the arrow below, you would have an abv of 45% and a proof of 90.

Each increment on the abv scale is 1.
Each increment on the proof scale is 2.

Reading at the meniscus. This is very important. The meniscus is the curved upper surface of a liquid in a tube. When you place the hydrometer into the distillate a meniscus will form around it. Make sure you read at the bottom of the meniscus, not at the part that rises up on the side of the hydrometer. The picture below shows how to read the proof on an alcohol hydrometer correctly. In this case the correct reading would be 164 proof.

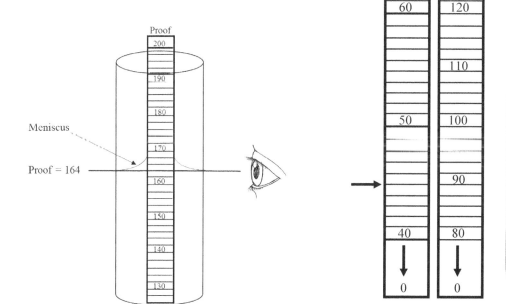

AJUSTING THE ABV FOR TEMPERATURES
ABOVE OR BELOW 15.5°C (60°F).

The alcohol hydrometer is calibrated to work at 15.5°C (60°F). If the temperature of your distillate is above or below 15.5°C (60°F) you need to make an adjustment to your reading. As the distillate temperature increases the alcohol becomes less dense, the hydrometer sinks lower into the distillate and you get a false high reading. You need to subtract from the hydrometer reading in order to get the correct abv. As the distillate temperature decreases the alcohol becomes more dense, the hydrometer rises and you get a false low reading. You need to add to the hydrometer reading in order to get the correct abv. The chart on page 20 shows you the amounts to add or subtract at the various distillate temperatures. Make sure you check the distillate temperature and don't use the ambient air temperature when making these adjustments. Check the distillate temperature by inserting your alcohol hydrometer into your parrot tube.

(Photocopy the chart and post it on the wall next to your still.)

ABV TEMPERATURE CORRECTION

Temp °F	0-25 Proof	25-50 Proof	50-200 Proof
100	-14	-12	-16
95	-12	-10.5	-14
90	-10	-9	-12
85	-8.5	-7.5	-10
80	-7	-6	-8
75	-5	-4.5	-6
70	-3	-3	-4
65	-1.5	-1.5	-2
60	0	0	0
55	+1.5	+1.5	+2
50	+3.5	+3	+4
45	+5	+4.5	+6
40	+7	+6	+8
35	+9	+8	+10
30	+10.5	+9	+12
25	+12	+10.5	+14
20	+14	+12	+16
15	+16	+13.5	+18
10	+18	+15	+20
5	+19	+16.5	+22
0	+21	+18	+24

Subtract from the abv reading when the distillate temperature is above 60°F.
Add to the abv reading when the distillate temperature is below 60°F.

20

SUGAR HYDROMETER (SACCHAROMETER)

A saccharometer is a hydrometer used for determining the amount of sugar in a solution. In the case of making whiskey, the sugar hydrometer is used to measure the specific gravity (SG) in the mash and the wash after fermentation is complete. Once we know the SG of the mash or the wash we can use the chart on page 22 to figure out the sugar content. We use this information to determine the potential alcohol in the mash and the wash. Potential alcohol (PA) is an estimate of the percentage of the mash or wash that will become alcohol from fermentation by the yeast. The sugar hydrometer has two scales, a specific gravity scale and a potential alcohol scale. The diagram on the right shows each scale. You can check the SG on the scale and also read the corresponding PA scale. It is more accurate however, to read the SG and use the chart on page 22 to identify the PA. When you purchase a sugar hydrometer a small version of the chart comes with it. A saccharometer can be purchased from a brew store or from Amazon.com for about $12.00.

READING THE SG AND PA

The more sugar that is in the mash or the wash the higher the SG will be. This means the density of the solution is higher. The higher the SG the higher the hydrometer will float in the solution. This will show a higher SG and PA reading on the hydrometer. As an example, look at the arrow on the right. The correct reading would be 1.070 for SG and 9.20 percent for PA. Again, using the chart on page 22 will give you a more accurate reading.

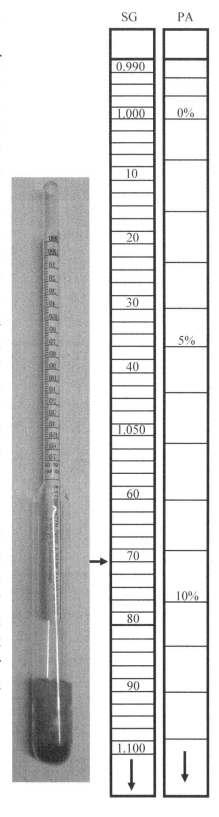

21

Specific Gravity and Potential Alcohol Chart

Specific Gravity (20°C/68°F)	Potential Alcohol (%/Volume)
1.000	0.0
1.005	0.7
1.010	1.3
1.015	2.0
1.020	2.6
1.025	3.3
1.030	4.0
1.035	4.6
1.040	5.3
1.045	5.9
1.050	6.6
1.055	7.2
1.060	7.9
1.065	8.6
1.070	9.2
1.075	9.9
1.080	10.5
1.085	11.2
1.090	11.8
1.095	12.5
1.100	13.2
1.110	14.

The saccharometer is calibrated to work at a temperature of 20°C (68°F). You need to know the temperature of your wort or your wash when taking a measurement. Use your long stem food thermometer to take the temperature. If the wort or wash is higher or lower the 20°C (68°F) use the following chart to adjust your reading. Most saccharometers come with this chart.

Temperature F°	Correction
54.2	- 0.002
61.5	- 0.001
68	-
73.7	+ 0.001
79.2	+ 0.002
84.3	+ 0.003

GRADUATED CYLINDER

The graduated cylinder is a necessary tool for using your hydrometers to measure specific gravity of your mash, wash and distillate. Remember that you are measuring the sugar content of your mash and wash in order to determine their potential alcohol. You are also measuring the abv of your distillate as you distill your wash. Fill the cylinder with fluid from your mash, your wash, or your still and place the appropriate hydrometer into the cylinder. A turkey baster works good for transferring fluid into the cylinder. Be sure to spin the hydrometer to eliminate any bubbles sticking to it. Just give it a slight spin, let it stop and take your reading. You can get a good graduated cylinder from a brew store or from Amazon.com for about $10.00.

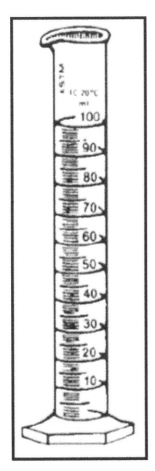

A graduated cylinder makes it easy to take your specific gravity measurements.

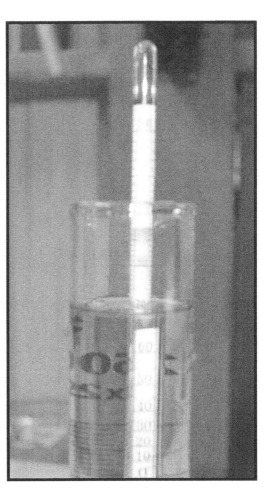

Using an alcohol hydrometer to measure abv in a graduated cylinder.

FIFTEEN GALLON COOKING POT WITH LID

The size of your cooking pot will depend on the size of your still and on how big of batches you plan to cook. I recommend a fifteen gallon, triple clad bottom pot. This will allow you to cook batches for a nine gallon (35 liter) still. Get a good quality pot with a triple clad bottom. The thick bottom of a pot like this will help prevent burning your mash on the bottom. A good quality cooking pot can be purchased at a brew store for about $85.00.

LARGE WOODEN STIRRING PADDLE

A nice large stirring paddle makes mash cooking much easier. You can also use large stirring spoons, but if you do, stirring your mash will be a lot more work. You can find a wooden paddle like the one pictured on Amazon.com for $15.00.

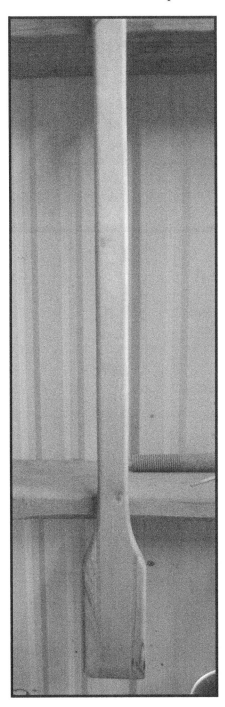

FOOD GRADE LONG STEM THERMOMETER

Used to check temperature of mash and distillate. Long stem thermometers are available at brew stores and Amazon.com for $10.00.

25

PROPANE BURNER FOR COOKING MASH
5 GALLON PROPANE TANK

The Bayou Country Classic propane burner is perfect for cooking large batches of mash. These are available at stores like Walmart, Lowe's, brew stores and like everything, at Amazon.com. They cost about $45.00. Propane tanks are available everywhere. They cost about $45.00.

ELECTRIC HOT PLATE BURNER

You need an electric burner with at least 1500 watts for distilling. If you get one that is less than 1500 watts it will take forever to heat your wash when distilling. A decent burner will cost around $50.00. They are available at most department stores and Amazon.com. Some people use propane burners for distilling. Extra precautions are needed if using an open flame .

EIGHT OUNCE CANNING JARS

You will need around twenty four 8 ounce canning jars. These will be used during the spirit run. The spirit run is the second distillation you will do on each batch. It is the run where you will be collecting the final product and dividing it into four ounce increments as you distill. This process will be explained in full detail in the distillation chapter. You can get canning jars at any department store for about $8.00 for a case of twelve.

ONE GALLON AGING JARS

Gallon jars can be used to store and age your whiskey. In the chapter on aging we will discuss the jar aging method that is an alternative to aging in oak barrels. I recommend buying four or five of them to start with. You can get them at brew stores for $5.00.

AGING JAR LABELS

It is really important to accurately label your aging jars or things will get mixed up and you won't know what you have in each jar. Photocopy the labels on page 29 and use them for labeling your jars.

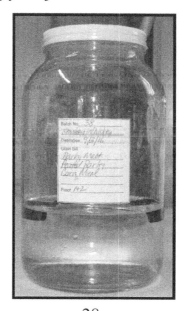

AGING JAR LABELS

Batch No_____ _____ Distillation_____ Grain Bill _____ _____ _____ _____ Proof_____	Batch No_____ _____ Distillation_____ Grain Bill _____ _____ _____ _____ Proof_____
Batch No_____ _____ Distillation_____ Grain Bill _____ _____ _____ _____ Proof_____	Batch No_____ _____ Distillation_____ Grain Bill _____ _____ _____ _____ Proof_____

Distillation: Date of spirit run.
Grain Bill: Each grain and percentage.
Proof: The aging proof. Normally 125.

DISTILLER'S ACTIVE DRY YEAST (DADY)

DADY is a good all-purpose yeast, in the Saccharomyces cerevisiae species, for whiskey making. This yeast will consistently produce eight to ten percent alcohol depending on the mash grain bill. Yeasts produce various compounds, including esters, during fermentation, that give the distillate different flavors. Once you become a seasoned whiskey maker you could experiment with different yeast strains. I think it's a good idea to start with DADY because it is reliable and far less expensive that other specialty yeast strains. You can by it from brew stores or from Amazon.com for about $10.00 a pound. This is enough for many batches depending on the size of your still.

YEAST NUTRIENTS

Yeast nutrients need to be added to your mash at the same time that you pitch the yeast. These nutrients are necessary for optimum yeast reproduction and growth. Healthier yeast means better fermentation and more alcohol production. You can buy yeast nutrients at brew stores or at Amazon.com for about $3.00 for a 2 ounce package or about $10.00 for a full pound.

AMYLASE ENZYME

Alpha-amylase enzyme is added to the mash to aid in the saccharification process. The enzyme breaks down starch molecules into single glucose and maltose molecules. Available at brew stores for $3.00.

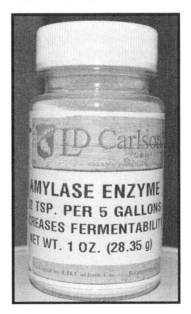

AMERICAN WHITE OAK CUBES

For jar aging you will need either toasted or charred American White Oak cubes. You can buy these at brew stores, but they are very expensive. At about $7.00 for a 2.5 ounce package, you are paying $44.80 for a pound of burnt wood. There are easy ways to produce your own wood cubes to use for aging your whiskey. This process is covered in the next section.

HOME MADE WHITE OAK AGING CUBES

To make your own charred aging cubes buy some white oak wood, char it with a propane torch or char it on a camp stove. If you want toasted aging cubes, place the wood in your oven at 400°F for about two hours. I cut the pieces up into approximately one inch cubes. The size isn't that important as long as they will fit into your aging jar. You can place the charred or toasted cubes into your gallon jars of newly distilled whiskey, put the lid on and let it age. Three one inch cubes is about the right amount. Leave the wood in until you get the color and flavor you want. You can always experiment with this. Remove the lid once a week to allow volatile vapors to escape. It is best to leave the lid on loosely.

Jar aging, by placing the wood into the whiskey, instead of placing the whiskey into a charred barrel, produces some excellent product in much less time. It takes about six months to produce the best product. Much less than the years it takes in a barrel. This is because you have a much greater surface area of wood per volume of whiskey in a gallon jar than you do in a barrel. We will discuss the aging process in more detail in the chapter on aging.

The next couple of pages will show you the process of making your own charred aging cubes.

Actual Size

Chunks of American White Oak wood

PROPANE TORCH CHARRING

One way to char your wood is to hold the wood with some metal tongs and burn it with your torch. Let it burn until you get a nice yellow flame going, it's good and black and cracks start to show. When finished, throw in into a bucket of water to cool it off. It's ready to go. Whiskeys are aged with different degrees of charring. Mild, moderate, and heavy are the most common degrees. You can experiment with this. You can buy a propane torch and tongs at most department stores. Propane torches are about $20.00 and metal tongs cost around $5.00.

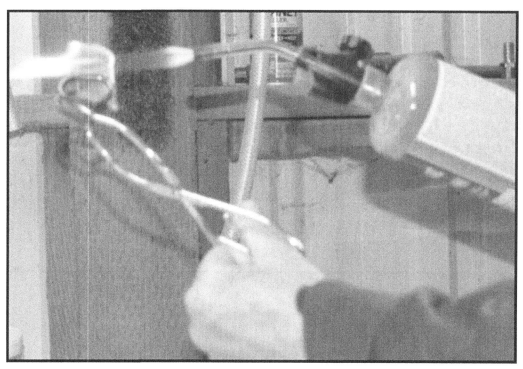

Charring a piece of White Oak with a propane torch.

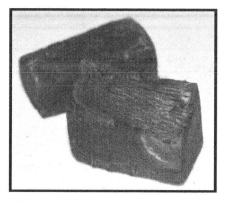

Charred White Oak Cubes

PROPANE CAMP STOVE CHARRING

Using a propane camp stove is the quickest way to char some White Oak wood. Place some chunks on the stove, fire it up and let it burn. You can turn the wood over a few times just like cooking a steak. When they're good and black and start cracking, they are finished charring. Propane camp stoves are available at camping stores and most department stores. A decent one costs about $40.00.

Charring wood on a camp stove.

Some charred White Oak wood. Break these into smaller pieces, say one to three inches long, and place them into your aging jar.

12 GALLON FERMENTING BUCKET WITH LID

A 12 gallon fermenting bucket is just the right size to use for a 35 liter still. To use a 35 liter (9 gallon) still you should plan to cook your batches with 8 gallons of water and 24 pounds of grain yielding about a 10 gallon mash. After fermentation you will end up with about 7 gallons of wash. This will fit perfectly into your 35 liter still. You shouldn't fill your still much more than about 3/4 full of wash for distilling. Note: You do not need to use a carboy and pressure valve to ferment your wort. We will discuss this in detail in the fermentation chapter. You can buy a 12 gallon fermentation bucket for about $30.00 at brew stores.

12 Gallon Fermenting Bucket with Lid

Remember: If you have a still with a different volume than 35 liters, you can just make adjustments to make your wort and wash fit your equipment.

MASH BAG

The mash bag is placed inside your fermenting bucket. After you have cooked your mash, it has cooled to about 24°C (75°F), you have pitched the yeast, mixed it well, and aerated the mash, you pour the mash into the bag. This makes it easy to remove the mash from the fermenting bucket once fermentation is complete. This will be covered in detail in the fermentation chapter. These cost $7.00 at brew stores.

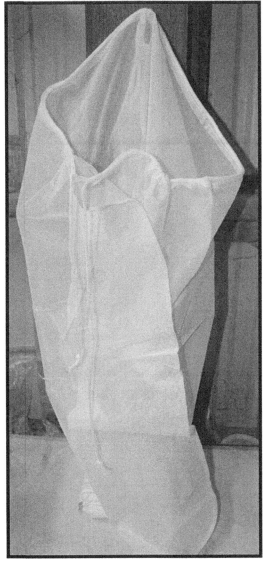

Mash poured into the mash bag which is in the fermentation bucket.

Mash Bag

FOOD SCALE

A good food scale is necessary for weighing your grain. You can get one at most department stores for about $40.00.

PLASTIC BOWL

A basic plastic salad or mixing bowl works well for measuring and weighing your grain, transferring grain into your cooking pot, transferring mash into your fermentation bucket and for transferring your wash into your still.

FLOUR FOR SEALING STILL HEAD

You will need to make a flour paste for sealing your still head. The head is removeable and must be sealed when distilling to prevent vapor loss. Mix 1 teaspoon of flour with about 1 teaspoon of water and mix it together. You should end up with a thick paste similar to pancake batter. Spread it around your still head seam with your finger and you are good to go.

Sealing the still head with flour paste.

KITCHEN STRAINER

A kitchen strainer is useful for taking samples of your wort when checking specific gravity. Place it into the mash pot to separate the wort from the grains.

TURKEY BASTER

Use a turkey baster to draw samples from your wort and your wash. The picture on the left below shows how to draw a sample of wort from the mash pot. The picture on the right shows drawing a sample from your fermentation bucket. Just place the turkey baster down in between the mash bag and the bucket. Draw it out and place it into you graduated cylinder, put your saccharometer in and read your SG.

FERMENTATION CHAMBER

You can ferment your wort in your home, shed, shop, or barn. The requirement is that you need to have a consistent temperature of between 21 and 27ºC (70 and 80ºF). A fermentation chamber is convenient and easy to build. The one shown below is made of plywood. It is 4 feet wide, 2 feet deep and 4 feet high. Line the inside walls and door with 1 inch thick insulation panels. The door latches shut and the temperature is controlled with a small space heater with a thermostat. It works great and you can fit 2 fermentation buckets inside. You can get the insulation panels at Lowe's or Home Depot for a couple of bucks each.

SPACE HEATER WITH THERMOSTAT

A small space heater with a thermostat makes it easy to control the temperature in your fermentation chamber.

5 GALLON BUCKETS WITH HANDLES

You will need two 5 gallon buckets for aerating your mash and transferring your fermented wash into your still.

STORAGE TUB WITH LID

A plastic tub works great for storing your supplies like hydrometers and other small items.

PLASTIC GARBAGE CAN WITH LID

A large garbage can is necessary to store your grains in. Keeps the mice away.

PLASTIC FUNNEL

A plastic funnel is used to pour your whiskey into bottles.

SHOP RAGS

Shop rags will be used throughout the whiskey making process. It's a good idea to have a few on hand for every batch you make.

ROPE

You will need about 6 feet of 3/8" rope to tie your mash bag to a 4X4 beam so it can drain once fermentation is complete.

4X4 WOOD POST

An 8 foot 4X4 works well for tying your mash bag up to for drainage.

DUCT TAPE

Duct is used for recording the temperature and abv of each jar during distillation. It is also handy for labeling your fermentation bucket when you have a batch ready to ferment.

DUCT TAPE

You will need duct tape for recording your temperature and abv as you distill using the 24 pint sized canning jars. Place a line of duct tape on the edge of a table as shown below. As you fill your small jars half full during distillation, you will place them on the table and record the vapor temperature and abv. This example shows the temperature in Celsius. Some stills have a Celsius vapor thermometer and some have Fahrenheit. You will be reading the abv from the alcohol hydrometer placed in your parrot.

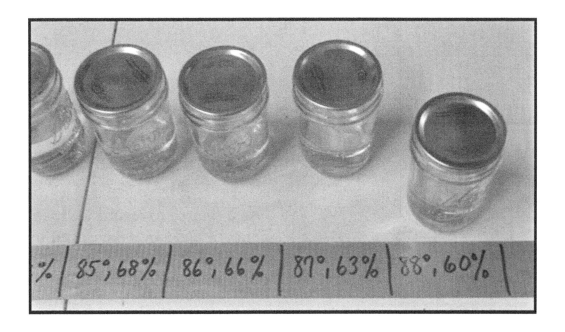

You will also need to record the batch number and date on your fermentation bucket. Duct tape works well for that also.

FOOD TONGS

Food tongs are used to hold pieces of white oak wood while they are being charred with a propane torch.

SHARPIE

Use a sharpie to record your temperature and abv when distilling and for labeling your fermentation buckets when fermenting.

COFFEE FILTERS

Coffee filters are used to filter your whiskey when the aging process is complete.

16 OUNCE MEASURING CUP (CLEAR)

You will need a measuring cup to measure the quantity of your distillate .

CLEANING STATION, HOSE

A wood bench, hose and running water are nice to have for cleaning and rinsing your equipment.

BLEACH

Bleach is used to sanitize your tools, 5 gallon buckets and fermentation buckets. Do not use bleach on any cooper equipment, it will corrode it.

WHITE VINEGAR

Vinegar works well for cleaning your still, alcohol parrot and anything made of copper. Pour about 2 cups into your still, add a gallon of water, scrub out the still and rinse with water 3 times.

SCRUBBER PADS

Scrubber pads work well for cleaning your still and other equipment.

PRODUCT RECORD

Keeping good records of each batch you make is EXTREMELY important. You need accurate data of each batch so that you can make improvements in your process and in case you want to duplicate a certain batch that you really like. I recommend using a three ring notebook and a product record sheet like the one shown below. This is a 2 page record. It is also set up as a step by step instruction sheet. Follow the steps and record your data as you go. Both pages are shown on pages 50 and 51. You should photocopy these and use them.

PRODUCT RECORD

Batch Number _43_   Name _Bourbon_

Grain Bill

Corn Meal – 60%, 14.4 lbs.   1 t Amylase Enzyme
Rye – 25%, 6.0 lbs.   5 t Yeast Nutrient
Barley Malt – 15%, 3.6 lbs.   5 t DADY
24 lbs.

Mash

Date _10/30/16_   Time _12:00 PM_   Water Qty _8 Gal._
Heat water to 167F. Gelatinize corn, 158 - 167F, 60 minutes. _162°F, 1:45 – 2:45 pm_

Heat mash back to 158F. Add other grains, amylase enzyme, rest at 148F for 90 minutes ___
Chill or rest overnight to 75 - 80F. _80 F_ Specific gravity _1.071_ Potential Alcohol _9.5 %_

Pitch Yeast

Date _10/31/16_ Time _11:30 am_ Mash temp. _80 °F_

Yeast Type _DADY_ Qty _5 t_ Yeast nutrients _✓_ Qty _5 t_

Stir, aerate - pour between 5 gallon buckets 3 times. Pour into fermentation bucket.

Fermentation

Ferment at 70 - 77F. About 3 days.
Stop when final specific gravity reaches 1.001.

Start Date _10/31/16_ Time _12:00 PM_ Starting SG _1.071_ Starting PA _9.5 %_
End Date _11/3/16_ Time _3:00 PM_ Ending SG _1.004_ Ending PA _1.5 %_

Stripping Run   Net PA _8.0 %_

Heat slowly. Keep heat low, 80 - 82C. Run to 96C or 10% abv. 10 Hours. Low Wines.

Date _11/6/16_ Start Time _9:30 am_ End Time _8:00 PM_ Distillate Temp ___

1st Drips: Time _11:30 am_ Temp _55°C_ Fast Drips: Time _12:00 pm_ Temp _70 °C_

Start abv _60%_ End abv _10%_ Final Blended abv _34%_ Qty _192 oz._

49

PRODUCT RECORD

Batch Number_____   Name_____

Grain Bill

_____

_____

_____

Mash

Date_____   Time_____   Water Qty_____

Heat water to 167°F. Gelatinize corn, 158 - 167°F, 60 minutes. _____

Heat mash back to 158°F. Add other grains, amylase enzyme, rest at 148°F for 90 minutes _____
Chill or rest overnight to 75 - 80°F. _____ Specific gravity_____ Potential Alcohol____

Pitch Yeast

Date _____   Time_____   Mash temp._____

Yeast Type_____   Qty_____   Yeast nutrients_____   Qty _____

Stir, aerate - pour between 5 gallon buckets 3 times. Pour into fermentation bucket.

Fermentation

Ferment at 70 - 80°F. About 3 days.
Stop when final specific gravity reaches 1.001.

Start Date _____   Time_____   Starting SG_____   Starting PA_____

End Date _____   Time_____   Ending SG_____   Ending PA_____

Stripping Run   Net PA _____

Heat slowly. Keep heat low, 80 - 82°C. Run to 96°C or 10% abv. 8 Hours. Low Wines.

Date_____   Start Time_____   End Time_____   Distillate Temp_____

1st Drips: Time_____   Temp_____   Fast Drips: Time_____   Temp_____

Start abv_____   End abv_____   Final Blended abv _____   Qty_____

Spirit Run   Batch No._____   Name_____

Use 24, 8 oz. jars. Fill half full. Heat slowly. Takes about 3 hours.

Date_____ Start Time_____ End Time_____ Added Water Qty_____

Distillate Temp_____ Dump first 8 ounce jar (methanol) _____

1st Drips: Time_____ Temp_____   Fast Drips: Time_____ Temp_____

Jar Data and Cuts (Temp and abv) Use 75% abv - 65% abv cuts for highest quality.

1_____   2_____   3_____   4_____   5_____   6_____

7_____   8_____   9_____   10_____   11_____   12_____

13_____   14_____   15_____   16_____   17_____   18_____

19_____   20_____   21_____   22_____   23_____   24_____

Heads Cut: ABV_____   Temp_____   Tails Cut: ABV_____   Temp_____

Total Qty_____   Finish ABV_____

Aging

Qty_____   ABV_____   Proof_____

Beginning Date_____   Ending Date_____

Toasted White Oak Cubes_____   Charred White Oak Cubes_____

Age at 125 proof, 62.5% abv. Age for 6 months for best product. Proof down (dilute) to drinking proof after aging. Use filtered water.

Proofing Down

Water Added_____   Final ABV_____   Final Proof_____

Filtering and Bottling Date_____   Coffee Filter_____   Total Final Qty_____

Final Notes

_____

_____

Chapter 3

Whiskey Grain Bills and Recipes

You've read the first two chapters and you have all the necessary supplies and equipment - it's time to make whiskey!

The first step is to decide on what kind of whiskey you want to make. For our example we will choose a standard bourbon grain bill and we'll use that example to show you each step in the whiskey making process. Everything we do will be calculated for a 35 liter (9 gallon) still. I recommend this size. It is easy to work with and will produce three to four fifths of final product per batch. If you have a different sized still it is easy to modify the grain bill based on the 35 liter still quantities.

Whiskey grain bills normally have from 2 to 3 lbs. of grain per gallon of water. I recommend using 3 lbs. of grain per gallon of water. For our example batch we will use 8 gallons of water and 24 lbs. of grain, (3 X 8 = 24 lbs. of grain). This will produce about 10 gallons of mash due to the added volume of the grain. Follow the cooking instructions in chapter 4 carefully! The amount of actual wash going into the still after fermentation will be about 7 gallons, just right for a 9 gallon still. You shouldn't fill your still much more than about three fourths full.

EXAMPLE BOURBON GRAIN BILL AND RECIPE
(for our whiskey production example in chapter's 4 - 11)
8 Gallons Water (10 gallons total mash volume - explained on page 53)
Corn Meal - 60%, 14.4 lbs. (.6 X 24)
Rye - 25%, 6.0 lbs. (.25 X 24)
Barely Malt - 15%, 3.6 lbs. (.15 X 24)
1 Teaspoon Amylase Enzyme (1/2 teaspoon per 5 gallons mash)
5 Teaspoons Yeast Nutrient (1/2 teaspoon per gallon mash)
5 Teaspoons Distiller's Active Dry Yeast, (1/2 teaspoon per gallon mash)

Note: On pages 55 to 57 of this chapter you will find more grain bills and recipes for Straight Bourbon, Smokey Bourbon, Wheated Bourbon, Single Malt Whiskey (Scotch), Irish Whiskey, Oat Whiskey, Rye Whiskey, Corn Whiskey and Chocolate Malt Whiskey.

HOW TO CALCULATE THE TOTAL MASH VOLUME

9 Gallon Still Example

To determine the amount of water needed figure about 90% of your still size.

.9 X 9 = 8.1 gallons of water (round off to 8 gal.)

The actual volume of mash will come out a little more than the amount of water you use. This is because the grains will add some volume to the total mash quantity. You can estimate the added volume from the grain by multiplying **.08** times the number of pounds of grain and adding it to the gallons of water. .08 is the estimated amount, in gallons, that one pound of grain will add to the total mash volume. The reason the grain adds only a fractional amount to the total mash volume is due to the porosity of the grain particles, or the air space between the particles. This space fills with water. The grain also absorbs some of the water as well.

8 gal. water X 3 lbs. grain = 24 lbs. grain needed

24 X .08 = 1.92 gal. added volume from grain (round off to 2 gal.)

8 + 2 = 10 gal. total mash volume

The question is, will the wash from this batch fit into your still? Remember, you don't want to fill your still more the 3/4 full. You will typically get about 70% of your total mash volume returned as wash.

10 gal. mash X .70 (percentage of wash recovered from mash) = 7.0 gal. wash

7/9 = .78

This wash will fill 78% of your still. Very close to 3/4 (75%) limit.
The 10 gallon mash will work.

The math calculations can help you meet the volume limits of your still. You don't need to meet those figures exactly. They are just guidelines. When cooking batches for your own still you will need to experiment and make adjustments as necessary.

BASIC STRUCTURE OF THE WHISKEY RECIPES

Grain Bill - Corn, Barley Malt, Rye, Wheat, etc.
Amylase Enzyme - 1/2 teaspoon per 5 gallons of mash
Yeast Nutrient - 1/2 teaspoon per gallon of mash
Distiller's Active Dry Yeast (DADY) - 1/2 teaspoon per gallon of mash
Yogurt (Optional) - 1 teaspoon per gallon of mash

HOW TO CALCULATE YOUR GRAIN QUANTITIES

BASIC STRAIGHT BOURBON

9 Gallon still example

8 Gallons of water
24 Pounds of grain (8 gal. water X 3 lbs. grain = 24 lbs. grain needed)
10 Gallon mash

Just multiply the percentage of each kind of grain in your grain bill by the total amount of grain required.

Corn Meal   60%,   14.4 lbs. (.6 X 24)
Rye   25%,   6.0 lbs. (.25 X 24)
Barley Malt   15%,   3.6 lbs. (.15 X 24)
Amylase Enzyme 1 t (1/2 teaspoon per 5 gallons mash)
Yeast Nutrient 5 t (1/2 teaspoon per gallon mash)
DADY 5 t (1/2 teaspoon per gallon mash)
Yogurt (optional) 10 t (1 teaspoon per gallon mash) - some distillers use yogurt as a source of Lactobacillus bacteria.

NOTE: You may notice different grain bills for Straight Bourbon. As long as they contain at least 51% corn and the rest of the grain bill contains rye and barley, it is considered Bourbon.

NINE GRAIN BILLS AND RECIPES
Follow the instructions in chapter's 4 through 11 for any of these recipes. For any recipes use the same procedures we used for our example batch.

STRAIGHT BOURBON - WOODFORD RESERVE STYLE

Corn Meal   72%
Rye   18%
Barley Malt   10%
Amylase Enzyme - 1/2 teaspoon per 5 gallons mash
Yeast Nutrient - 1/2 teaspoon per gallon mash
DADY - 1/2 teaspoon per gallon mash
Yogurt (optional) - 1 teaspoon per gallon mash

SMOKEY BOURBON

Corn Meal   60%
Rye   20%
Barley Malt   15%
Peated Barley   5%
Amylase Enzyme - 1/2 teaspoon per 5 gallons mash
Yeast Nutrient - 1/2 teaspoon per gallon mash
DADY - 1/2 teaspoon per gallon mash
Yogurt (optional) - 1 teaspoon per gallon mash

WHEATED BOURBON

Corn Meal   60%
Barley Malt   20%
Rye   10%
Wheat   10%
Amylase Enzyme - 1/2 teaspoon per 5 gallons mash
Yeast Nutrient - 1/2 teaspoon per gallon mash
DADY - 1/2 teaspoon per gallon mash
Yogurt (optional) - 1 teaspoon per gallon mash
Lighter, sweeter taste than straight bourbon. (The ladies like it!)

SINGLE MALT WHISKEY (SCOTCH)

Barley Malt   90%
Peated Barley   10%
Amylase Enzyme - 1/2 teaspoon per 5 gallons mash
Yeast Nutrient - 1/2 teaspoon per gallon mash
DADY - 1/2 teaspoon per gallon mash
Yogurt (optional) - 1 teaspoon per gallon mash

IRISH WHISKEY

Barley Malt   50%
Ground Barley   50%
Amylase Enzyme - 1/2 teaspoon per 5 gallons mash
Yeast Nutrient - 1/2 teaspoon per gallon mash
DADY - 1/2 teaspoon per gallon mash
Yogurt (optional) - 1 teaspoon per gallon mash

Distill 3 times - one stripping run, two spirit runs

OAT WHISKEY

Oats (quick rolled)   80%
Barley Malt   20%
Amylase Enzyme - 1/2 teaspoon per 5 gallons mash
Yeast Nutrient - 1/2 teaspoon per gallon mash
DADY - 1/2 teaspoon per gallon mash
Yogurt (optional) - 1 teaspoon per gallon mash

RYE WHISKEY

Rye   60%
Barley Malt   20%
Corn Meal   20%
Amylase Enzyme - 1/2 teaspoon per 5 gallons mash
Yeast Nutrient - 1/2 teaspoon per gallon mash
DADY - 1/2 teaspoon per gallon mash
Yogurt (optional) - 1 teaspoon per gallon mash

CORN WHISKEY

Corn Meal   80%
Barley Malt   20%
Amylase Enzyme - 1/2 teaspoon per 5 gallons mash
Yeast Nutrient - 1/2 teaspoon per gallon mash
DADY - 1/2 teaspoon per gallon mash
Yogurt (optional) - 1 teaspoon per gallon mash

CHOCOLATE MALT WHISKEY

Barley Malt   75%
Chocolate Barley Malt   25%
Amylase Enzyme - 1/2 teaspoon per 5 gallons mash
Yeast Nutrient - 1/2 teaspoon per gallon mash
DADY - 1/2 teaspoon per gallon mash
Yogurt (optional) - 1 teaspoon per gallon mash

The chocolate barley malt is just a darker roasted barley. There is no actual chocolate in it. The whiskey will have a subtle chocolate note.
Very Delicious!

Chapter 4

Cooking the Mash

WE WILL USE THE EXAMPLE BOURBON GRAIN BILL
AND RECIPE FROM PAGE 52. YOU CAN USE THIS
PROCESS FOR ANY RECIPE.

**STEP 1: PUT 8 GALLONS OF WATER INTO YOUR
COOKING POT**

STEP 2: HEAT THE WATER TO 75°C (167°F).

STEP 3: ADD THE CORN MEAL AND GELATINIZE

For any grain bill that includes corn, the corn must be gelatinized. Put in 14.4
lbs. of corn meal. Stir constantly as you add the corn or you will get corn dough
balls that are hard to mix in. Once it is well mixed, put the lid on the pot and let
it sit for one hour. You want to keep the temperature between 70°C (158°F) and
75°C (167°F). The corn mash will get very thick. It will liquefy after you mix in
the barley malt and amylase enzyme later on.

Mix the corn in thoroughly. A
couple of minutes of stirring
will do the job.

Put the lid on and let rest
for one hour.

STEP 4: ADD THE REMAINING GRAINS

Heat the mash back to 70°C (158°F).
Add 6 lbs. of rye, stir it into the mash.
Add 3.6 lbs. of barley malt, stir it into the mash.
Once you mix in the other grains the temperature will drop to approximately 148°F, this is where you want to be. Add some heat if necessary.

Adding grain to the mash pot.

STEP 5: ADD THE AMYLASE ENZYME

Amylase enzyme is added at the rate of 1/2 teaspoon per 5 gallons of mash. For this batch of 10 gallons add 1 teaspoon. Mix everything together well. A few minutes of good mixing will do.

STEP 6: COOL THE MASH OR LET IT REST OVER NIGHT TO COOL

Place the lid on your pot and let the mash rest for 90 minutes or overnight. You only need to keep the temperature at 64°C (148°F) for 90 minutes. If you're going to leave it overnight just bring it to 64°C (148°F) then let it rest until the next morning. This is where saccharification is occurring. Next, we need to cool the mash down to about 24°C (75°F). You can use a wort chiller after 90 minutes or you can let the mash rest overnight, either way works. The goal is to allow the temperature to drop down to around 24°C (75°F). This is the temperature at which you will pitch your yeast.

STEP 7: CHECK THE SPECIFIC GRAVITY OF THE WORT

Once the wort has cooled to between 24 and 27°C (75 and 80°F), place your kitchen strainer into the mash bucket to separate some wort from the grain. Using your turkey baster draw some wort and place it into your graduated cylinder. Fill it to within about 3 inches of the top. Use your saccharometer to check the specific gravity of the wort. It should read somewhere around 1.080 which equates to a potential alcohol of 10.5%. Your actual SG could be a little less or a little more. Your potential alcohol should be between 8 and 11%. Every batch will vary by a small amount. Not to worry. Record your SG and PA in your distillation record.

Drawing out some wort using a kitchen strainer and turkey baster.

Placing the wort into the graduated cylinder.

Placing the saccharometer into the graduated cylinder and reading the SG.

Chapter 5

Fermentation

STEP 1: SANITIZE YOUR BUCKETS, MASH BAG, PLASTIC BOWL, FERMENTATION BUCKET AND LID

Pour about 1 tablespoon of bleach into one of your 5 gallon buckets. Add a couple of gallons of water. Use that to wash out your other 5 gallon bucket, your mash bag, your plastic salad bowl and your fermentation bucket and lid. Rinse off everything with running water. I recommend doing this outside of your building with a hose. Use the triple rinse method. That is, rinse everything off or out three times.

STEP 2: PLACE YOUR MASH BAG INTO THE FERMENTATION BUCKET AND TIE IT IN PLACE

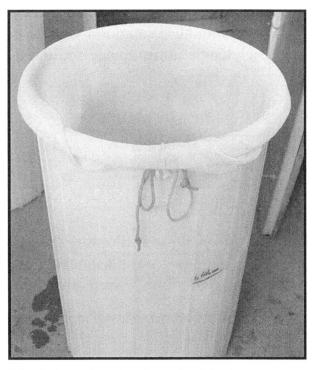

Mash bag tied in place inside the fermentation bucket.

61

STEP 3: ADD THE YEAST NUTRIENTS

You need 1/2 teaspoon of yeast nutrients per gallon of mash. Put 5 teaspoons of yeast nutrient into your mash pot. Mix it in well.

STEP 4: PITCH THE YEAST

You will use 1/2 teaspoon of yeast per gallon of mash. Get your yeast from the refrigerator, place 5 teaspoons in a small plastic bag or bowl and let it warm to room temperature for about 15 minutes. You don't want to pitch cold yeast into a batch of warm wort, the quick temperature change could kill the yeast.
Mix the yeast in well.

Pouring the yeast in from a small plastic bag that was allowed to warm up to room temperature.

STEP 5: AERATE THE MASH

Remove the mash using your plastic bowl. It is much easier to do it with a bowl in small amounts rather than trying to lift and pour your whole cooking pot. Pour bowls of mash into a 5 gallon bucket until the bucket is about half full. Next pour the mash between your two five gallon buckets three times. This will aerate the mash. After aerating pour the half bucket into your fermentation bucket. Keep doing this until the mash pot is empty and all of the mash is in your fermentation bucket.

Pouring mash from the cooking pot into a 5 gallon bucket.

Aerating the mash by pouring between two buckets three times.

STEP 6: POUR THE MASH INTO YOUR FERMENTATION BUCKET

Pouring mash into the fermentation bucket.

Using the 10 gallon mash recipe, as we are for this example batch, will end up filling your fermentation bucket up to about 4 inches from the top. The grain cap will rise almost to the top of the bucket. This is perfect and maximizes production for the size of your equipment.

STEP 7: PUT THE LID ON YOUR FERMENTATION BUCKET AND LABEL IT

STEP 8: PUT THE FERMENTATION BUCKET INTO YOUR FERMENTATION CHAMBER

Set your heater at 24 to 27°C (75 to 80°F) and close the door. Fermentation has begun.

Chapter 6

Procedures During Fermentation

CHECK FOR THE GRAIN CAP AND CRACKLING SOUND

Check your batch after the first 2 to 3 hours. Pull the lid off of the fermenting bucket. You should see the grain cap. When the yeast really start growing and producing CO_2, a grain cap will form at the top of the fermentation bucket. This is a good sign because it shows that the yeast are actively fermenting. You should also be able to hear a distinct crackling sound, like Rice Krispies in a bowl of milk. That is the sound of the CO_2 bubbling up to the surface.

Grain Cap

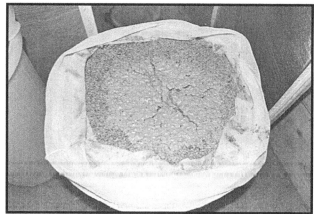

Grain Cap

CHECK TEMPERATURE OF FERMENTATION CHAMBER

Check the temperature of your fermentation chamber each day. You want it to stay around 24° to 27°C (75° to 80°F).

CHECK THE SG OF THE WASH

Fermentation should be complete in about 3 or 4 days. After 3 days take a SG reading with your saccharometer. The SG should be close to 1.000 when fermentation is complete.

When your SG is at 1.000 or close to it, all or most of the glucose has been converted to alcohol and the yeast are dying off. You will not the hear the crackling sound any longer and the grain cap may have sunk back into the wash. Fermentation is complete at this point. It's time to pull the mash bag and recover the wash.

Remove the lid off of your fermentation bucket. Pull the mash bag in a few inches in order to separate the wash from the grain. Draw wash out using your turkey baster and fill your graduated cylinder up to about 3 inches from the top.

Filling the graduated cylinder with wash.

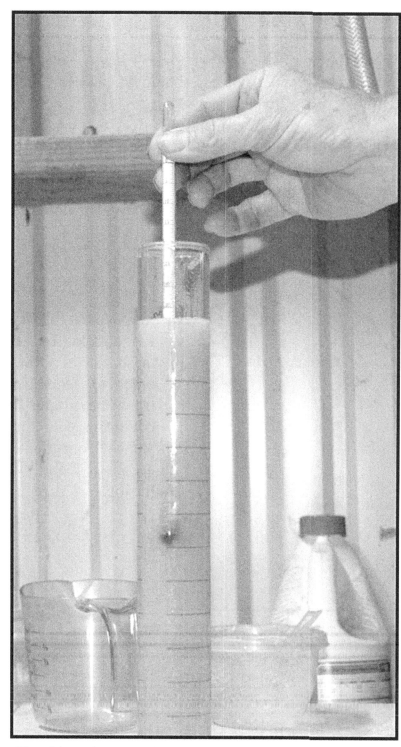

Checking the SG of the wash with a saccharometer. If it's at 1.000 or close to it fermentation is complete.

Chapter 7

Recovering the Wash

The wort, which was the liquid with the mash, has been fermented and is now called the wash. It will contain between 8 and 10% alcohol. Our task now is to separate the wash from the grain and prepare for distillation.

STEP 1: OPEN YOUR FERMENTATION BUCKET AND TIE A ROPE AROUND THE TOP PART OF THE MASH BAG

STEP 2: PULL THE BUCKET UNDERNEATH A
SOLID 4X4 BEAM

The beam should be about 4 feet high laying horizontally between two supports.

4X4 support beam laying across the corner of a rail fence. This is a good setup for hanging your mash bag to drain out the wash before distillation.

Mash bag in place underneath the 4X4 beam.

STEP 3: PULL UP THE MASH BAG AND TIE IT TO THE 4X4

Put the rope over the top of the 4 X 4 and slowly pull the mash bag up so that the wash can drain back into the fermentation bucket. Wind the rope around the 4 X 4 several times and tie it off so the bag will not slip back into the bucket. You can let it drain overnight or you can squeeze the liquid out of the mash bag. When it is finished draining you will end up with about 7 gallons of wash in your fermentation bucket. After it settles you will see about an inch layer of dead yeast in the bottom, this is called the lees. You can dump the lees or leave them in the wash when you distill. Some believe the lees add flavor to the distillate. It's a personal choice.

Mash bag tied to a 4 X 4 on top. This allows the wash to drain from the mash bag into the fermentation bucket.

71

Chapter 8

First Distillation - Stripping Run

Now the fun part begins, seeing your product start to flow. The stripping run has the sole purpose of getting all of the alcohol out of the wash. That includes the good stuff and the not so good stuff. Follow the steps outlined in this chapter and your stripping run will be a success.

STEP 1: REMOVE THE WASH FROM THE FERMENTATION BUCKET

Remove the mash bag from your fermentation bucket. This will require untying it from the 4 X 4 beam and setting it aside out of your way. Next, begin ladling out the wash into a five gallon bucket with your plastic bowl. Fill the bucket about half way with wash. Pour the wash from the bucket into your still. Keep doing this until all of the wash is in the still.

Removing the wash from the
fermentation bucket.

STEP 2: POUR THE WASH INTO THE STILL

Each time you collect about half a bucket of wash pour it into your still. If your still is located close enough to your still you could just ladle the wash directly from the fermentation bucket. Otherwise, moving the wash to the still with a 5 gallon bucket works very well.

Pouring the wash into the still.

STEP 3: ATTACH THE HEAD ONTO THE STILL AND FASTEN THE CONDENSER TUBE

Place the still head on top of the still. Fasten the still head tube to the condenser tube. If your still has a fastening nut for connecting the head tube to the condenser tube, tighten it by hand, doesn't need to be too tight. Using the side of your hand, lightly pound the still head into place on the still. You want the still head to sit squarely onto the still with the seam even all the way around.

Fastening the still head tube to the condenser tube.

Lightly pounding the still head in place.

STEP 4: SEAL THE STILL HEAD

Make up some flour paste and seal your still head.

Sealing the still head with flour paste.

STEP 5: SET UP 1 GALLON COLLECTION JAR AND ALCOHOL PARROT

For the stripping run you will use a 1 gallon jar to collect the distillate. Place the jar on a small table or small wooden box so it sits below you condenser. Place the food grade condenser collection tube into the top of your parrot. Position the parrot tube so that distillate will flow into your gallon jar from the parrot. Place your alcohol hydrometer inside the parrot as shown.

Correct still setup. Food grade tube from the condenser goes into the top of the alcohol parrot. The alcohol hydrometer is correctly placed into the parrot. The parrot is positioned to allow distillate to flow into the 1 gallon collection jar.

(See detail enlargement on page 77)

This picture shows the food grade condenser tube feeding into the top of the parrot, the correct placement of the alcohol hydrometer and the correct positioning of the parrot so that distillate will flow into the collection jar.

STEP 6: TURN ON YOUR BURNER

The goal is to heat up the wash slowly. If you heat it up too fast you could burn the wash and you could vaporize the liquid too fast. This would result in too high a concentration of water coming through with your alcohol. So go slow! As the run progresses you will need to increase the temperature a little at a time. You will know it is time to increase the temperature when the distillate dripping rate slows way down. It will take about 3 hours before you see any distillate dripping from your collection tube. Then things will speed up.

STEP 7: TURN ON THE CONDENSER WATER LINE

Turn on your water line to the condenser immediately before or after turning on your burner. Just a trickle will do. The water will slowly come in through the bottom waterline and will slowly trickle out of the top outlet line. This will keep your condenser water cool enough to liquefy the vapor coming from the still. You must make sure the incoming water is cold. Also make sure your outflow line is set up to drain outside or into some kind of drain.

STEP 8: COLLECT THE DISTILLATE

You should see your first drips of distillate after about 3 hours. The vapor temperature will be around 60°C (140°F). When your parrot fills with distillate you will be able to start observing the abv. It will start at around 60%. The vapor temperature will quickly rise to around 80°C (176°F). Try to keep the temperature around this level for as long as you can by adjusting your burner. The temperature will slowly increase and the abv will slowly decrease as the run continues. Monitor your abv and keep distilling until the abv has dropped to 10%. Your vapor temperature will be around 95°C (203°F) at this point. You can distill all the way down to 0% abv, but there is not much alcohol at that point, mostly water. I recommend stopping the run at 10% abv. The entire run for a 7 gallon wash will take about 8 hours. I recommend having other things to do with your time during the stripping run. You just need to keep checking on the still as the run proceeds.

You should collect approximately 1.5 gallons of distillate from the stripping run. This is called the "low wines." The blended abv will be around 30%. Label your collection jars with the following: Stripping Run, Batch Number, Date. Keep these in a safe place until you are ready to do the spirit run.

Collecting distillate during the stripping run.

80

Chapter 9

Second Distillation - Spirit Run

The purpose of the spirit run is to collect and further refine the alcohol from the low wines. As discussed in chapter 1 there are several kinds of alcohol in the distillate. Our job is to separate these out and collect the ethanol which will be made into whiskey. We need to separate the run into three fractions, heads, hearts and tails. The hearts are the good stuff, ethanol, that we want to keep for drinking.

STEP 1: CLEAN YOUR STILL

After the stripping run is finished you need to clean your still. You can use alcohol or white vinegar, but don't use bleach on anything made of copper. It will corrode the copper. I recommend vinegar.

Pour about a pint of vinegar into your still, add a couple of gallons of water and scrub out your still with a dish scrubber pad. Rinse out your still 3 times with a hose. Do the same for your still head. You should also pour some vinegar through you alcohol parrot and rinse it out good.

The main thing you are getting rid of when cleaning your still is copper sulfate ($CuSO_4$). When you are distilling the vapors in the still contain sulfur. The sulfur binds with the copper your still is made of and creates copper sulfate. The copper sulfate binds to the interior of your still. This is a very beneficial reaction because it removes the sulfur from your distillate. This greatly improves the taste of your product. The only negative thing is you need to clean the copper sulfate out of your still after each use. Some vinegar, water and moderate scrubbing will do the job.

STEP 2: PUT A LINE OF DUCT TAPE ON YOUR TABLE

This will be for recording the temperature and abv for each of your small collection jars as the run progresses. It is important to collect the distillate in 4 ounce increments and record the temperature and abv. This will help you make the heads, hearts and tails cuts when the run is finished.

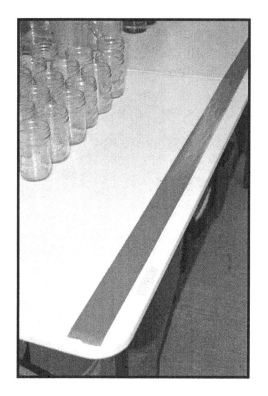

STEP 3: GET YOUR 8 OUNCE MASON JARS READY

Rinse out your jars and have them ready to go. Once the distillation gets going you will be filling jars and setting up new ones about every 10 minutes.

STEP 4: POUR THE LOW WINES INTO THE STILL

Take your low wines jars and pour them into your still. Your low wines should have an abv that is lower than 40%. If you have a batch of low wines that are higher than 40% abv you should add some purified water and dilute it down. Check the abv again with your alcohol hydrometer.

STEP 5: PUT YOUR STILL BACK TOGETHER

Put the still head back on. Connect the still head tube to the condenser. Reseal the head with flour paste.

STEP 6: TURN ON THE CONDENSER WATER LINE

You want just a trickle of water coming in through your water line. The amount coming in must equal the amount going out through the outflow line on top of the condenser. The goal is to keep the water in the condenser cool.

STEP 7: SET UP YOUR FIRST COLLECTION JAR

This jar will be used to collect the first 7 ounces of your spirit run. ***This will include the foreshots and should be dumped.*** It will contain methanol and other undesirable alcohols. ***Do not use your parrot to collect this first jar.*** You don't want methanol in your parrot.

REMEMBER:

All of the numbers you are seeing are based on our example 10 gallon batch. You would need to adjust things for a different sized batch.

STEP 8: TURN ON YOUR BURNER

For the spirit run you can start off with medium high heat and turn it down when the temperature begins to rise to about 70°C (158°F).

STEP 9: COLLECT DISTILLATE IN YOUR FIRST JAR

Remember, you are not using the alcohol parrot at this step. Collect directly into your first jar, the one you are going to dump. At about 60°C (140°F) you will start to see slow drips of distillate. It will take about half an hour for this to start. The temperature will slowly rise. Then the temperature will spike to around 78°C (172°F) and the speed of the drips of distillate will increase. You want a fast dripping of distillate, but not a steady steam. If you get a stream you will not be separating the different fractions of alcohol correctly. Turn the temperature down a little if this happens. When the first jar has close to 7 ounces of distillate in it get ready to pull it. I like to be on the safe side and recommend dumping 1 full ounce per gallon of wash which would be 7 ounces for our example batch. Dump this first jar and check it off on your product record sheet so you know you have completed this important step.

Collecting the first jar of distillate. This will contain methanol and will be dumped. ***Do not use your parrot.***

STEP 10: PUT THE ALCOHOL PARROT AND A NEW JAR IN PLACE AND COLLECT DISTILLATE

After discarding the foreshots put your parrot under the distillate tube from your condenser. Put your second jar under the parrot tube to collect the distillate. It will take a few minutes for the parrot to fill with distillate and start dripping. This is helpful because it gives you some time to get your next jar in place. Put your alcohol hydrometer into the parrot. As the second jar fills your still vapor temperature will be around 80°C (176°F) and your abv will be around 80%. Monitor your burner and try to keep it around 80°C (176°F). As the run continues the temperature will slowly rise and the abv will slowly drop. Monitor your burner and adjust as necessary to keep a steady drip of distillate.

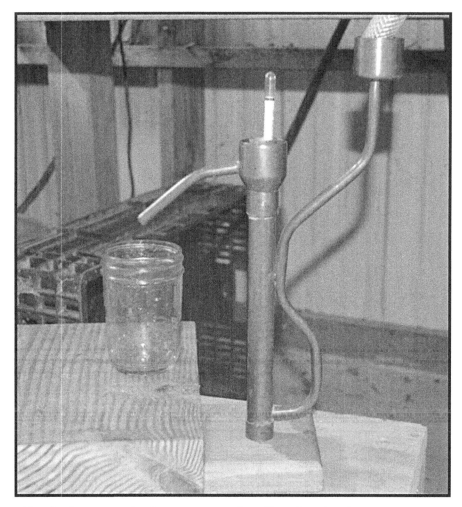

Alcohol parrot, hydrometer and collection jar in place for the spirit run.

STEP 11: CONTINUE COLLECTING 4 OUNCE QUANTITIES AND RECORDING DATA

As each jar fills to about half full, 4 ounces, replace the jar with an empty one and place the full one on your table by the duct tape. Record the temperature and abv of each jar as shown below.

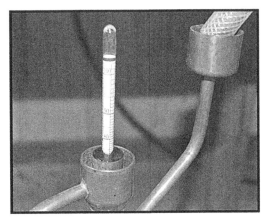

Check the abv for each jar as they fill.

Check the vapor temperature as each jar fills.

The picture shows a jar half full of distillate with the correct data recorded on the duct tape. This one had a vapor temperature of 81°C (177.8°F) and an abv of 80%. We are dividing the run into 4 ounce increments so it will be easier the make the heads, hearts and tails cuts when the run is finished.

Keep filling your jars and recording the data until the run is finished. The picture on page 88 shows you what the run will look like as it progresses.

As the run progresses your table will look the one in the picture. Each jar in a line with the temperature and abv recorded on the duct tape. You could end up with as many as 24 jars depending on when you decide to stop the run.

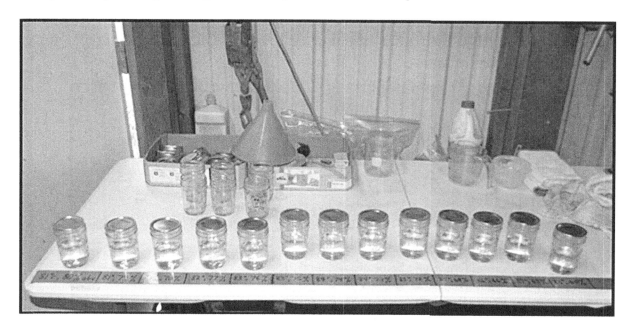

STEP 12: STOPPING THE SPIRIT RUN

There are several options for when to stop your spirit distillation run. You could continue to distill until there is zero alcohol coming out of your still, in other words, 0% abv. However, this is really not worth the effort. If you decide to distill out most of the tails in the batch and put them into your next spirit run, you could distill down to 10% abv. If you don't want to keep the tails for the next distillation, you could stop the run at the point where you think the tails have started in the run, possibly as early 65% abv if you use the 75/65 cuts. I recommend distilling until 10% abv and keeping the tails to put into the next spirit run. The reason for doing this is that there is still some ethanol in the tails that could be recovered in a subsequent run and the tails also contain esters which add unique flavors to your whiskey.

We will discuss making the cuts between heads, hearts and tails in step 13.

STEP 13: MAKING THE CUTS

Making the cuts refers to where in the spirit run you are going to make the divisions between heads, hearts and tails. There are some standard cuts that are used by commercial distillers that can be helpful in deciding where to make your cuts. The guideline I recommend is called the middle fifth cut used by the Glenmorangie Distillery in Scotland. They use a 75/65 cut. This means everything in a run that is above 75% abv is designated as heads. Everything that is below 65% abv is designated as tails. So everything from 75% to 65% abv is designated as hearts. This is considered to be a very tight cut, thereby producing a very high quality ethanol containing very little heads and very little tails. Of course, if you want a little more volume, you could use the general commercial distillery cuts of 75/55. If you do, you will need to be careful not to get to much tails in your final product or it will ruin the run.

In addition to using an abv percentage there are two important considerations when making your cuts, taste and smell of the distillate. You need to smell the distillate in the jars and dip your finger in and taste them. The following information will help you with that process.

Heads
Will have a strong, fruity odor and will have a strong taste with a bite.
Contain acetone, acetaldehyde, acetate and some ethanol.

Hearts
Will smell light and sweet. They will have a smooth sweet taste.
Contain primarily ethanol - the good stuff.

Tails
Will smell light a wet dog. They will taste muddy and awful. As soon as the tails start you will be able to smell them in your distillate.
Contain fusel oils including propanol, butanol and amyl alcohol. Also contain proteins, carbohydrates, fatty acids, esters and some ethanol.

After you have made your cuts and separated out your hearts you can blend in some heads and tails to adjust the flavor of your final product to your liking. It takes time to learn how to blend distillate correctly. When first learning to distill I suggest you stick with aging your hearts without any blending. After you get some experience under your belt you could start experimenting with blending.

The skill is being able to sniff out and taste where the heads end and where the tails begin. Use the 75/65 cuts as a guide. Your actual runs may come out a little different than that, but it will give you a starting point.

This picture shows the heads cut marked on the duct tape. All of the jars with an abv more than 75% will be poured into a separate container and labeled "heads." On the other end, all jars with an abv less than 65% will be poured into a separate container and labeled "tails." The heads and tails will be added to the next spirit run of the same grain bill. That way you can distill out some more of the ethanol that remains.

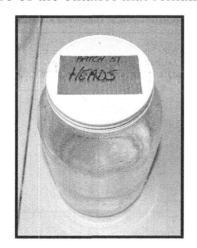

STEP 14: SEPARATE OUT THE HEARTS

Pour all of your small jars of hearts into a one gallon jar. Using a funnel, pour some hearts distillate into your graduated cylinder and measure the abv with your alcohol hydrometer. Next, measure the total volume in ounces using your measuring cup. Be sure to record this information in your product record. You will need this data later on when you proof down (dilute) your final product.

Pouring hearts into a one gallon jar.

A funnel was used to fill the graduated cylinder with blended hearts.

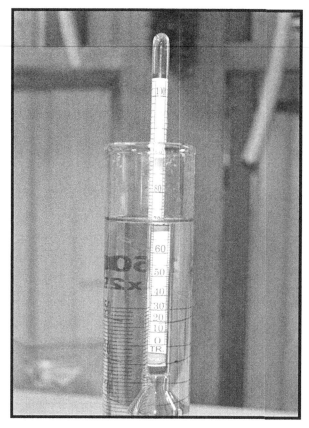

Checking the hearts abv with an alcohol hydrometer.

Measuring the quantity of hearts with a measuring cup.

Chapter 10

Aging Your Whiskey

Aging your distillate is the step that actually creates whiskey. Commercial distilleries use charred oak barrels to age their product. Barrels or casks made of American White Oak wood are the most commonly used structures for aging whiskey, although there are some variations to that. Oak barrels are expensive, large (53 gallon), and take years to properly age the whiskey. An alternative to barrel aging is jar aging. This requires one gallon glass jars with lids and either charred or toasted American White Oak cubes. The process is quite simple and will create excellent product in six months or less. We covered the process of making your own charred or toasted cubes in chapter 2.

STEP 1: PROOF DOWN (DILUTE) YOUR WHISKEY TO 125 PROOF (62.5% abv)

The best proof for aging is supposed to be 125 or 62.5% abv. Although you will find some variations to that in the literature. You will need to add purified water to your whiskey in order to do this. Do not use regular tap water, it could taint the flavor of your whiskey. Use either bottled water or filtered tap water. Go to the following website for a good dilution calculator. ***homedistiller.org/calcs/rad14701*** Just plug in the numbers and it will show you how much water to add to your whiskey to proof it down to the desired abv.

STEP 2: POUR THE PROOFED DOWN WHISKEY INTO AN AGING JAR

STEP 3: ADD YOUR WHITE OAK CUBES TO THE JAR

Three or four one inch cubes will do the job. You can experiment with this and see what works best for you.

STEP 4: LABEL THE JAR

Photocopy and use the labels on page 29 to label your jar. Store in a safe place. Open the lid once a week to release volatile vapors.

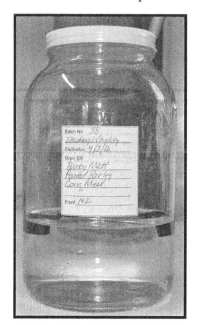

Chapter 11

Bottling Your Whiskey

Your whiskey will be ready to bottle when the color and taste are to your liking. It will normally take a minimum of two months. Of course, the longer you let it age the better it will be. I recommend six months for the best product. When the time arrives, get out your bottles, your funnel and some coffee filters. It is best not to filter whiskey through activated carbon of charcoal filters, they will strip out too many congeners and dilute the flavor of your whiskey.

STEP 1: PROOF YOUR WHISKEY DOWN TO THE DRINKING PROOF YOU WANT

Decide what proof you want for your whiskey, 80, 90, etc. Measure the volume of whiskey in your jar. Some is always lost due to evaporation during the aging process. Use the dilution calculator at **http://homedistiller.org/calcs/rad14701**. Plug in the numbers and it will tell you how much water to add to your whiskey for the proof your want. Use purified water for proofing down.

STEP 2: RINSE OUT YOUR BOTTLE (EVEN NEW ONES)

STEP 3: FILTER YOUR WHISKEY INTO THE BOTTLE

STEP 4: PUT THE CORK IN

STEP 5: ATTACH YOUR LABEL

I recommend designing a label on your computer with MS Publisher. Print the label on plain paper. Cut it out and glue it onto your bottle using a glue stick. The glue stick works well and it is easy to remove the label when you need to recycle any bottles. See the examples on page 97.

Using nice bottles makes your whiskey look even better!

Filtering whiskey into a bottle. Note: This picture is black and white. The whiskey is actually a beautiful amber color!

EXAMPLE LABELS

COPPER CREEK

Bourbon Whiskey

90 Proof

Batch No:
Distillation Date:

COPPER CREEK

Barley Whiskey

90 Proof

Batch No:
Distillation Date:

Chapter 12

Cleaning and Sanitizing
Your Equipment

BLEACH

Use about 1 tablespoon of bleach per gallon of water for cleaning/sanitizing your non-copper equipment. Do not use bleach on cooper items, it will corrode the metal. Use a bleach solution for your mash cooking pot, five gallon buckets, fermentation bucket and lid, mixing paddle, jars and plastic bowl. Just wipe down the items with the bleach solution and triple rinse. Rinsing three times is a good practice to make sure all of the bleach solution is removed from the item being cleaned.

WHITE VINEGAR

Use white vinegar and water to clean your still, condenser and alcohol parrot.

Outside of Still
Mix 1 tablespoon of salt, 1 cup white vinegar and enough flour to make a paste.
Apply to the outside of your still.
Let it sit for 30 minutes.
Wash off with cloth and water.

Inside of Still
Light Cleaning
A light cleaning is all that is necessary most of the time.
Put about 1 gallon of water and 2 cups of vinegar into your still.
Scrub out the still with a scrubber pad.
Triple rinse.

Inside of Still
Thorough Cleaning
After every 10 distillation runs I recommend a thorough cleaning.
Put 2 gallons of water and 1/2 gallon of vinegar into your still.
Put the still head on, connect your condenser and run the still.
Heat the solution up to boiling and let it run through your system for 10 minutes.
Don't forget to set up a collection jar or you'll have hot vinegar water all over the floor.
Triple rinse.

Chapter 13

Safety

Distilling spirits is actually very safe if common sense is applied. Here are some of the critical items to keep in mind when distilling.

1. DO NOT LEAVE YOUR STILL UNATTENDED.

2. USE AN ELECTRIC HOT PLATE TO HEAT YOUR STILL.
   A propane burner can be used with proper precautions.

3. KEEP YOUR CONDENSER WATER COOL.

4. HIGH PROOF ALCOHOL AND VAPOR ARE VERY FLAMMABLE.

5. DO NOT FILL YOUR STILL MORE THAN 3/4 FULL.

6. DISCARD THE FORESHOTS - THEY CONTAIN METHANOL.

7. KEEP A FIRE EXTINGUISHER NEARBY.

8. SEAL ALL LEAKS IN YOUR SYSTEM WITH FLOUR PASTE.

9. MAKE SURE TO HAVE GOOD VENTILATION.

10. USE GLASS DISTILLATE COLLECTION JARS - NEVER PLASTIC.

11. DIRECT THE DISTILLATE AWAY FROM YOUR STILL.

Glossary

Alcohols in the Distillate

There are a number of different types of alcohol produced by the yeast during fermentation. When we distill the wash the different kinds of alcohol will vaporize at different temperatures. The list below shows the different alcohols that are distilled out of a typical wash and the temperature at which each is vaporized.

Acetone 56.5°C (134°F)

Methanol 64°C (147°F) - ***Poison***

Ethyl acetate 77.1°C (171°F)

Ethanol 78°C (172°F)

2-Propanol (rubbing alcohol) 82°C (180°F)

1-Propanol 97°C (207°F)

Water 100°C (212°F)

Butanol 116°C (241°F)

Amyl alcohol 137.8°C (280°F)

Furfural 161°C (322°F)

Alcohol By Volume (ABV)

Alcohol By Volume is usually abbreviated as ABV. It is the concentration of total alcohol, as a percentage, in the distillate or in a bottle of whiskey.
For example, 40% ABV.

Alpha-Amylase Enzyme

Alpha-amylase enzyme is an enzyme produced by germinating seeds or grain like barley. The enzyme helps break down long chained sugars (starch) into smaller carbohydrates containing one, two, or three glucose molecules. These can then be fermented by the yeast. The picture below illustrates the structure of a starch molecule. The enzyme breaks the bonds in between the glucose molecules.

Starch Molecule

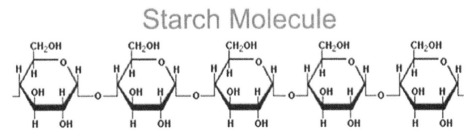

Glucose molecules bent into rings and linked together

Angel's Share

The spirit lost to evaporation out of the oak barrels during aging. About 2% of the spirits are lost to evaporation each year.

Back Set

The watery part at the end of a distilled batch of wash that can be added into the next batch.

Bacteria

Bacteria are microscopic single-celled organisms. There are many kinds of bacteria, some are harmful, but many are beneficial. There are several species of Lactobacillus bacteria that can enter your mash naturally or can be added intentionally. Lactobacillus will produce various acids that are used in the creation of esters in the wort. The esters will have a flavorful effect on your whiskey. You can purchase Lactobacillus bacteria to incorporate into your mash if desired.

Barley

The scientific name for barley is Hordeum vulgare. There are two main varieties, 2 row and 6 row. Two row barley has 2 rows of grain kernels on each head. It has a lower protein content, but higher carbohydrate (sugar) content. This is the primary kind used to make barley malt.

Six row barley has 6 rows of grain kernels per head. It has more protein and a lower sugar content. It is primarily used as livestock feed.

Beta-Amylase Enzyme

Beta-amylase is an enzyme also produced by germinating seeds or grains. The enzyme breaks chemical bonds at the end of the sugar chains (starch). This process produces two-chained sugars like maltose. It is an important process in whiskey making because is helps facilitate the saccharification process. The picture below shows a molecule of maltose which is made of two glucose molecules.

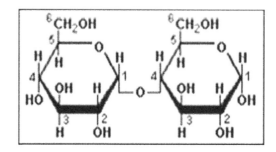

Bourbon

The grain bill for bourbon is corn, barley and rye. It must be at least 51% corn. Most commercial bourbons are made from 70-80% corn, 15-20% barley malt and 5-10% rye. Bourbon must be aged a minimum of 2 years in new charred American white oak barrels.

Cask Strength

The abv of whiskey as it is being aged in a cask. Also known as barrel proof. Aging proof is normally between 120 and 130 proof. The most popular aging proof is 125 (62.5% abv).

Congeners

Congeners are substances other than ethanol that are produced during fermentation. They can effect the flavor of the distillate positively or negatively.

Copper Sulfate (CuSO$_4$)

When distilling with a copper still, sulfur, produced by the yeast during fermentation, binds with the copper to produce copper sulfate. This is good because it removes the sulfur from your distillate. When you clean your still the copper sulfate is washed away.

Corn

The scientific name for corn is Zea mays. There are 6 different types of corn in the Zea mays genus that are produced and used by humans, dent corn, flint corn, pod corn, popcorn, flour corn and sweet corn. Yellow dent corn (Zea mays var. indentata) is the primary corn used for ethanol and therefore whiskey production. Yellow dent corn has a high starch content compared to other varieties and that characteristic makes it good for making spirits.

Corn Whiskey

The grain bill for corn whiskey must contain at least 80 percent corn. The remaining 20 percent is usually malted barley. Corn whiskey must be aged for a minimum of two years in new or used white oak barrels. The barrels don't have to be charred. Corn whiskey is often marketed as "White Lightening."

Cutting

Diluting the whiskey by adding water. Also known as proofing down. It is customary to cut the whiskey after aging is complete, since whiskey is aged at about 125 proof. This brings the proof of the whiskey down to a drinkable level.

Distillation

Distillation is the process of separating substances from a liquid mixture by heating, evaporating (forming a vapor), cooling and condensing vapor back into a liquid. Once the vapor is condensed back into a liquid it is referred to as the distillate. In the case of making whiskey the distillate is alcohol, primarily ethanol. The distillate produced during the whiskey making process starts off clear as water; this is true for any kind of spirit.

Esters

Esters are compounds produced during fermentation. They result from the combination of alcohols and fatty acids or acetates. Esters add aromas and flavors to the spirit. The primary ester found in the hearts of spirit distillations is ethyl hexanoate which has an apple-like aroma.

Ethanol

Ethanol, also known as ethyl alcohol, has the chemical formula C_2H_5OH and is one of the alcohols produced by yeast during sugar fermentation.

Feints

The final distillate from a spirit run. The feints are low in alcohol and can be added to the next run and redistilled.

Fermentation

Fermentation is the process of converting sugars, like glucose and maltose, into acids, carbon dioxide (CO_2), and various alcohols by yeasts. The alcohol we are primarily interested in is ethanol ($2\ C_2H_5OH$). During both respiration and fermentation yeast cells break down glucose molecules to release energy. This is called glycolysis. The breakdown of glucose also releases carbon atoms which can be used by the yeast to grow and reproduce (budding). It is important to make sure the yeasts have an ample supply of oxygen and other nutrients for efficient fermentation.

Foreshots

The first few ounces of distillate produced during a distillation. They contain methanol and other volatile alcohols. I recommend discarding one ounce per gallon of wash from the spirit run. Better to be on the safe side. So, if we had 7 gallons of wash after fermentation, we would discard the first 7 ounces of foreshots from the spirit run.

Gelatinization

When using corn meal or polenta as your source of corn in a batch, the corn must first be gelatinized. This involves heating the corn in water which breaks the bonds between the starch molecules. This basically dissolves the starch and allows the corn to absorb more water. The mixture will become very thick. Once the corn is gelatinized you can add the remaining grains (e.g., barley malt, rye) and proceed to cook the batch. This process will be explained in detail later.

Glucose, Maltose, Maltotriose

Glucose, maltose and maltotriose are the components of the starches found in the endosperm of cereal grains. Glucose ($C_6H_{12}O_6$) is the simplest sugar and is known as a monosaccharide meaning one glucose molecule. Maltose ($C_{12}H_{22}O_{11}$) is a disaccharide with two glucose molecules. Maltotriose ($C_{18}H_{32}O_{16}$) is a trisaccharide consisting of three glucose molecules. These sugars are present in the wort and are used by the yeasts during the process of fermentation.

Grain

Grain refers to the seed produced by plants in the grass family (gramineae). Most distilled spirits are made from grains including corn, barley, rye, wheat, oats and triticale. Although spirits can be made from pretty much any kind of organic matter containing carbohydrates, the grains are the most popular.

Grain Anatomy

It is important to have a basic knowledge of grain anatomy in order to understand how alcohol is produced from fermented grains. Refer to the picture below as we discuss grain anatomy. This diagram shows a generic example of a grain (seed). It could be barley, rye, oats, or wheat. Although corn is also in the gramineae family, its structure is a little different than the other grains. The endosperm contains starch (carbohydrates). When water enters the seed, enzymes are activated that convert the starch to glucose (simple sugar). The embryo (germ), which is an immature plant, feeds on the glucose and water and begins to grow (germination). It is the glucose we seek for our whiskey making endeavors. Glucose provides yeast with an energy source that facilitates the process of fermentation.

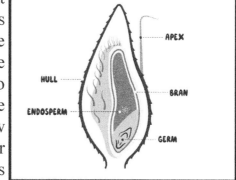

Grain Bill

In the distilling industry the grain bill is simply a list of which grains are used to make the mash and the percentage of each. For example, the grain bill for Jack Daniels Tennessee Whiskey is 80% corn, 12% rye and 8% malted barley. Of course, trying to make Jack Daniels whiskey isn't just a matter of using their grain bill. They use various techniques in their production process that produces the unique flavors of Jack Daniels, techniques that are closely guarded secrets.

Grain Cap

The layer of grain pushed up by carbon dioxide produced by yeast during fermentation. You will see a grain cap form at the top of your fermentation bucket.

Heads

The first major part of the distillate is called the heads. The heads contain compounds like acetone, acetaldehyde, acetate and some ethanol. They have a strong, almost fruity smell and taste harsh. Heads can be discarded or collected and added to the next spirit run. Approximately 20-30% of the liquid collected during a distillation run will be heads.

Hearts

The hearts contain mainly ethanol and are the part of the spirit run we want to collect and make into whiskey. Hearts will have a light sweet smell and a light sweet, smooth taste. Be warned though, hearts still do not taste like whiskey, they are still raw distillate. The skill of the distiller is in developing the ability to smell and taste the different fractions of distillate in order to separate the heads, hearts and tails effectively. Approximately 30-40% of the run will be hearts.
See Appendix A for an illustration of Heads, Hearts and Tails.

Irish Whiskey

Irish whiskey is obviously made in Ireland. The grain bill is 50 percent barley and 50 percent barley malt. The big difference is that Irish whiskey is triple distilled. Three distillations give the final product a very clean taste. It is aged in charred white oak barrels.

Lees

The layer of dead yeast that accumulates in the bottom of the fermentation bucket or vat. Some distillers say you should distill the lees with the wash and others say the lees should be left out of the distillation. It is the distiller's choice.

Malted Barley

Malted barley, or barley malt, is made by soaking barley in water and initiating the germination (sprouting) process. The grain is then heated with hot air in order to stop germination. During this partial germination beta-amylase enzyme is produced inside the grain that helps convert starches in the grain into simple sugars like maltose and glucose. When malted barley is mixed with other grains in the mash the beta-amylase enzyme, plus alpha-amylase enzyme added by the distiller, converts all of the starches from all of the different grains in the mash into glucose. Malted grains, like malted barley, are often referred to as malt, referring to the maltose in the grain.

Mash

The mash consists of water, grains and enzymes added to help in the Saccharification process. The mash is heated to specific temperatures and is rested for a certain length of time before adding yeast. The mashing process will be explained in greater detail later in the book.

Moonshine

Moonshine is illegal whiskey made at home. It can be made of any kind of organic matter, however, moonshine is typically made from corn mash and is not aged. Back during the days of prohibition, between 1920 and 1933, the production and sale of liquor (spirits) was illegal in the United States. People would illegally distill spirits at night, in the "shine of the moon," to avoid being caught by the law. The term is thought to have originated in England. Early English whiskey smugglers were called "Moonrakers" because they worked by the light of the moon. You can find whiskey called Moonshine in liquor stores, but it is not actually moonshine. It is simply white dog (white whiskey) that has not been aged in an oak barrel.

All distilled spirits start off as plain old ethanol, including moonshine. Ethanol is the good part of the distillate that can be made into whiskey and consumed. The various kinds of alcohol, including ethanol, come out of the still as clear as water. It's the different grains, the aging process, and filtration techniques that turn the ethanol into whiskey.

Oats

Oats, Avena sativa, are used to make bread, oatmeal, other baked goods and as livestock feed. There are a few distillers who make oat whiskey. The grain bill is usually 85% oats and 15% barley malt. Oats create a very smooth whiskey with a mellow, sweet, toasted grain flavor.

Peat and Peated Barley

Peat consists of dead plant material including moss, grasses and tree roots that have been compacted under a layer of soil and decomposed slowly over many years, sometimes thousands of years. The peat is dug up, dried and can be burned for fuel or other uses.

In whiskey making peat is burned underneath a layer of malted barley. The heat from the burning peat stops the germination of the malted barley and dries it out. The peat smoke produces chemicals called phenols that are absorbed by the malted barley and give it a smoky flavor. Peated barley is often used in making Scotch or other malt whiskeys. Regular malted barley is dried without using peat and does not have the smoky smell or flavor.

Pitching Yeast

Putting yeast into a mash.

Potential Alcohol

This is the amount of alcohol we would expect to be produced from the fermentation of the wort. Most batches of wort will have between 8 and 10% potential alcohol.

The Process of Making Whiskey

This is a very short description of the whiskey-making process to get us started. First, a mixture of grains, or other organic biomass, is mixed with water and cooked to form a mash. The mash is cooled and yeast is added so that sugars in the mash can be converted into alcohol (fermentation). The resulting fermented liquid (wash), which now contains alcohol, is heated in order to separate the various kinds of alcohol out of the wash (distillation). The distillate is aged with charred or toasted oak to produce whiskey. This process is basically the same, with some variations, for whiskey, bourbon, rum, vodka and single malt whiskey (Scotch).

Proof

Alcohol proof is twice the percentage of alcohol by volume. So if you have a whiskey that is 40% abv it would be 80 proof.

Rum

Rum is made from sugar and/or molasses. There are three main types of rum: white, gold and dark. White rum is not aged and it is filtered which removes much of the color and flavor. Gold rum is also known as amber rum. It is aged in charred white oak barrels. Dark rum is aged in charred white oak barrels for a longer period of time. Caramelized sugar is often added to add color and flavor.

Rye

Rye is another cereal grain in the gramineae family. It's scientific name is Secale cereale. Rye is used to make four, rye bread, rye beer, whiskey, vodka and is also used as livestock feed. Rye can be used to make rye whiskey, is part of the grain bill in bourbon, and is often used in making Canadian whiskey. It provides a spicy flavor to the whiskey. Early whiskey's in the United States were primarily made of rye since it was grown extensively at the time and was cheap. As the production of other grains like corn increased, other types of whiskey became more popular.

Saccharification

The breaking apart of polysaccharides (complex sugars and starches) to soluble sugars like glucose is called saccharification. Malted barley containing beta-amylase enzyme, and the addition of alpha-amylase enzyme to the mash, break the starch molecules apart to produce single molecules of glucose (simple sugar). The glucose can then be consumed by the yeast during fermentation.

Scotch

To be called Scotch, whiskey needs to be made in Scotland. Scotch is made from 100 percent malted barley. Some Scotches also have some peated barley in the mash. This gives the whiskey the smoky or peaty flavor. Scotch is aged a minimum of three years in charred white oak barrels. The best Scotch is made from a single batch of malted barley and not blended with any other batch. This is called single malt whiskey. In America whiskey made from 100 percent malted barley is called Single Malt Whiskey since it can't be called Scotch.

Single Barrel

Single barrel whiskey (or single cask whisky), is whiskey that comes from an individual aging barrel, instead of being created by blending together the contents of different barrels.

Small Batch Whiskey

Small batch whiskey is whiskey that is produced by mixing the contents of a small number of selected barrels. So, it is blended whiskey.

Sour Mash

Sour mash is mash from a previous batch that is added to a new batch of mash. This adds to the flavor of the whiskey and also helps to control bacteria like Clostridium butyricum which can ruin the batch.

Tails

The tails occur at the end of the run. Tails do contain some ethanol as well as fusel oils like propanol, butanol and amyl alcohol. Tails also contain water, carbohydrates and proteins. You will know when the tails start because they smell like a wet dog and taste muddy. You will also see an oily sheen on top of the distillate as the tails continue to distill and the distillate will start to look cloudy. Tails can be discarded or collected and added to the next spirit run. Tails will make up approximately 20-30% of a spirit run.

Tennessee Whiskey

Tennessee whiskey is basically bourbon, but it has been charcoal mellowed. That means it has been slowly seeped though a vat of sugar maple charcoal before going into an aging barrel. The addition of this step in the process makes it illegal to call the whiskey "bourbon." An example is Jack Daniel's Tennessee Whiskey.

Vodka

The name vodka comes from the Russian word "voda" which means water. Vodka is usually distilled at least three times. It is considered to be a neutral spirit, meaning it has very little flavor. Vodka can be made from anything that can be fermented as opposed to whiskey which must be made from grain. Most vodkas are made from grains or potatoes. Most commercial vodka distilleries make their finest vodkas from winter wheat. Vodka is not aged in barrels like whiskey.

Wash

The wash is the liquid produced after fermentation is completed. The wash will normally contain 8 to 10% alcohol. The wash goes into the still for distillation.

Wheat

Wheat, Triticum aestivum, is the second most produced grain in the world, topped only by corn. There are only a few straight wheat whiskeys produced in the world. However, there are many whiskeys which are "wheated", meaning that a small percentage of the grain bill includes wheat. Wheat tends to make whiskey smoother and sweeter tasting. The flavor profile of wheat whiskey is much milder than whiskey without wheat.

White Dog

The alcohol that comes out of the still and is placed into aging barrels is called white dog. It has no color and little whiskey flavor at this point. It is the raw distillate.

Whiskey

The word whiskey comes from the Latin word "aqua vitae," meaning the water of life. Whiskey is a distilled spirit made from fermented grain or any other organic matter containing carbohydrates. The distillate is aged in charred white oak barrels to produce whiskey. Remember that whiskey is a general term for various types of distilled spirits including bourbon, scotch, Tennessee whiskey, Canadian whiskey and Irish whiskey. They are all whiskey, but involve some different production and aging processes. We will cover each kind in more depth later in the book.

Wort

The wort is the liquid produced from the mashing process. It contains glucose which will be fermented by yeast. By using a sugar hydrometer we can measure the specific gravity of the wort and determine what is known as the potential alcohol level.

Yeast

Yeasts are the microorganisms that ferment the wort and create alcohol. Yeasts are single-celled microorganisms classified as members of the fungi kingdom. Saccharomyces cerevisiae is the primary species of yeast used in the distillation of spirits, however, there are many strains of yeast used within that species by the different distilleries. I recommend Distiller's Active Dry Yeast (DADY). This is a good all purpose yeast for distilling that works very well. Once you become an experienced distiller you can branch out and try different strains. Adding yeast to the mash is called "pitching" the yeast. Keep your yeast in an airtight container in the refrigerator.

Yeast Energizer

Yeast energizers contain components such as diammonium phosphate, yeast hulls, magnesium sulfate, vitamin B complexes and tricalcium phosphate. Energizers are used to give a boost to a fermentation that is sluggish or stuck during the fermentation process.

Yeast Nutrients

The source of energy consumed by yeast is glucose, but yeast also requires other nutrients in order to reproduce and grow. Yeast nutrient blends contain a mix of trace elements, inorganic nitrogen, organic nitrogen, zinc and phosphates that helps yeast grow and complete fermentation. Yeast nutrients are added to the mash at the same time as the yeast is pitched.

Yogurt

Some distillers use plain yogurt or other sources of Lactobacillus bacteria in their mash recipes. It is believed that Lactobacillus will produce various acids that will be made into esters by the yeast during fermentation. These esters have a positive impact on the flavor of the spirits. You can experiment with this.

APPENDIX

Appendix A

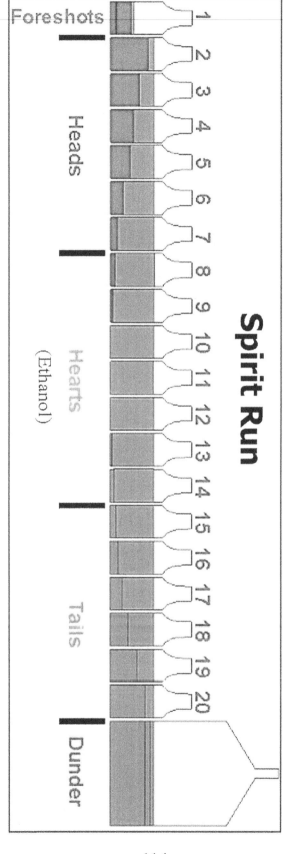

This graphic illustrates how there is ethanol in the heads and tails part of the spirit run. But, the highest concentration of ethanol is clearly in the hearts or middle part of the run.

114

Appendix B

Summarized Whiskey Making Instructions

1. Select your grain bill, page 52.

2. Calculate mash volume, page 53.

3. Cook the mash, page 58.
   - Put water into cooking pot
   - Heat water to 75°C (167°)
   - Add corn
   - Gelatinize corn 1 hour
   - Heat back to 70°C (158°F)
   - Add remaining grains
   - Add amylase enzyme
   - Rest at 64.4°C (148°F) for 90 minutes or overnight
   - Cool the mash to 24° - 27°C (75° - 80°F)
   - Check SG of the wort, record in your product record

4. Fermentation, page 61.
   - Sanitize equipment
   - Place mash bag into fermentation bucket
   - Put yeast nutrients into mash pot, mix
   - Pitch yeast, mix
   - Aerate mash with 5 gallon buckets three times
   - Pour mash into fermentation bucket
   - Put lid on fermentation bucket and label
   - Put fermentation bucket in fermentation chamber
   - Turn on space heater and adjust to keep temperature between 75° - 80°F

5. Procedures During Fermentation, page 66.
   - Check batch for grain cap and crackling sound after about 3 hours
   - Check fermentation chamber temperature each day
   - Check SG after 3 days

6. Recovering the Wash, page 69.
   - Open fermentation bucket
   - Tie rope around top of mash bag
   - Pull fermentation bucket underneath your 4X4 beam
   - Tie the mash bag to the 4X4 beam
   - Let the mash bag drain overnight or squeeze out the wash

7. Stripping Run - 1st Distillation, page 72.
   - Remove the wash from the fermentation bucket
   - Pour the wash into your still
   - Attach head onto still
   - Seal the still head with flour paste
   - Set up 1 gallon collection jar and a alcohol parrot
   - Turn on burner
   - Turn on water line to condenser
   - Collect distillate until 10% abv

8. Spirit Run - 2nd Distillation, page 81.
   - Clean your still
   - Put a line of duct tape on your table
   - Get 8 ounce jars ready
   - Pour low wines into your clean still
   - Put head on still
   - Seal still head with flour paste
   - Turn on water condenser line
   - Set up first collection jar - no parrot
   - Turn on burner
   - Collect distillate in first jar - discard

- Put parrot in place
- Place alcohol hydrometer into parrot
- Put empty 8 ounce jar in place
- Continue colleting distillate in 4 ounce quantities
- Record temperature and abv on duct tape for each 4 ounce jar
- Stop the run when tails begin
- Make your cuts - heads, hearts, tails
- Measure the quantity of hearts
- Measure the abv of the collected hearts
- Pour all of the hearts into a gallon jar

9. Aging Your Whiskey, page 93.
   - Proof your whiskey down to 125 proof (62.5% abv)
   - Pour whiskey into aging jar
   - Add toasted or charred American White Oak cubes
   - Label jar

10. Bottling Your Whiskey, page 95.
    - Proof your whiskey down
    - Rinse out your bottles
    - Filter whiskey into bottles using coffee filters
    - Put cork in bottle
    - Attach label to bottle

Appendix C

Equipment and Supply List

Alembic Pot Still and Parts (35 liter/9 gallon recommended)
1/2" Black Irrigation Tubing
1/2" Hose Clamps (3)
1/2" Food Grade Tubing
Alcohol Parrot
1 Gallon Distillate Collection Jar s (2)
Alcohol Hydrometer
Sugar Hydrometer
Graduated Cylinder
15 Gallon Cooking Pot with Lid
Large Wooden Stirring Paddle
Food Grade Long Stem Thermometer
Large Propane Burner - for cooking mash
5 Gallon Propane Tank
Electric Hotplate Burner - for distilling
8 Ounce Canning Jars (24)
1 Gallon Aging Jars (several)
Aging Jar Labels
Distiller's Active Dry Yeast (DADY)
Yeast Nutrients
Amylase Enzyme
American White Oak Cubes - Toasted or Charred, Purchased or Home Made
Propane Torch or Propane Camp Stove for Charring
12 Gallon Fermenting Bucket with Lid
Mash Bag
Food Scale
Large Plastic Bowl
Flour
Kitchen Strainer
Turkey Baster
Fermentation Chamber (Optional)
Space Heater with Thermostat

5 Gallon Bucket (2)
Storage Tub with Lid
Plastic Garbage Can with Lid
Plastic Funnel
Shop Rags
Rope (10 feet)
4X4, 8 Foot
Duct Tape
Food Tongs
Sharpie
Coffee Filters
16 Ounce Measuring Cup
Cleaning Station, Hose
Bleach
White Vinegar (Gallon)
Scrubber Pads
Product Record, Notebook

About the Author

Mr. Yorke has a Bachelor of Science Degree in Agriculture and a Bachelor of Arts Degree in Economics from Washington State University, Pullman, WA. He also has a Masters Degree in Technical Education from City University, Seattle, WA. Mr. Yorke taught High School Agriculture Science, Animal Science, Agricultural Biology and Horticulture for 32 years in SW Washington State.

Mr. Yorke learned the distilling process at a licensed craft distillery in Washington State.

Made in the USA
Monee, IL
26 August 2022

12534860R00072